'You're not

spinster.'

'No. You're wr
have romantic fantasies, I have nightmares! Would you like to know why? Would you really like to know why I'd never put such ideas into your daughter's head, why I haven't been making a play for you?'

Dear Reader

As summer gives way to autumn, this is a good time to reflect on how you feel about your loved ones. Being in love can be the most wonderful feeling on earth, yet why is it that so many people are frightened of expressing that love? That's certainly the case between our hero and heroine, yet, as in life, once expressed, it can lead to the greatest happiness. I think there's a lot to be learned in our books. Have fun learning . . .!

The Editor

Jennifer Taylor was born in Liverpool, England, and still lives in the north-west, several miles outside the city. Books have always been a passion of hers, so it seemed natural to choose a career in librarianship, a wise decision as the library is where she met her husband, Bill. Twenty years and two children later, they are still happily married, she is still working in the library, with the added bonus that she has discovered how challenging and enjoyable writing romantic fiction can be!

Recent titles by the same author:

PROMISE ME LOVE

LOVE IS THE ANSWER

BY

JENNIFER TAYLOR

MILLS & BOON

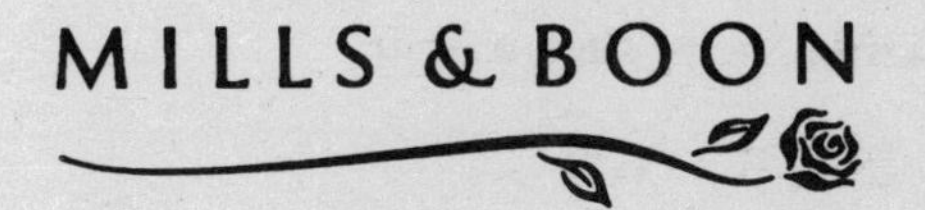

MILLS & BOON LIMITED
ETON HOUSE, 18-24 PARADISE ROAD
RICHMOND, SURREY TW9 1SR

First published in Great Britain 1993
by Mills & Boon Limited

This edition 1993

ISBN 0 263 78266 2

Set in Times Roman 10 on 12 pt.
01-9310-53349 C

Made and printed in Great Britain

CHAPTER ONE

THE phone rang once, twice. Sarah gripped the receiver, feeling the tension growing inside her. She'd met James MacAllister twice, and neither occasion had made her think that he would take what she had to tell him well. Not that she could blame him, of course. No parent would...

'MacAllister.'

The voice was brusque and deep, the harshness unmistakable even through the crackly connection. Sarah had a sudden, vivid mental picture of the last time she'd seen him three months before, his dark eyes like ice, his lean face rigid with barely restrained anger, and a shiver ran down her spine. She should have asked her colleague Mrs Lawrence to ring him instead of her. It had only been her sense of duty that had demanded she should make the call herself.

'Can I help you?' There was rough impatience in his voice now, and Sarah felt colour stain her cheeks as she realised she was only making matters worse by wasting time.

'Mr MacAllister, this is Sarah Marshall. I don't know if you remember me. I teach your daughter, Catherine.'

'I remember, Miss Marshall.' There was no mistaking the edge to his reply. He hadn't appreciated her comments a few months ago and it was obvious that he still hadn't forgiven or forgotten them. However, there was no time to dwell on that as he continued, 'Has something happened? Is that why you're calling?'

'I...I...' What was it about him that made her so nervous? She was used to dealing with both pupils and parents alike, yet James MacAllister had only to speak and she found herself stammering like a teenager rather than a mature woman of thirty who held down a responsible job. Annoyed with herself, Sarah hastened to continue, all too conscious of the impatience coming from the man at the other end of the line.

'I'm afraid Catherine has disappeared, Mr MacAllister.'

'Disappeared? What the hell do you mean? She was supposed to be on a study trip to France!'

'She was. I mean, she is.' Sarah took a deep calming breath. 'That's where I'm phoning you from: Paris.'

'Then I suggest that you tell me exactly what's been going on there. I didn't give permission for my daughter to go on the trip so that you could lose her!'

'I haven't lost her! And nothing has been going on apart from the schedule we'd planned!' He was obviously upset, so she shouldn't resent his curtness, his dictatorial manner in demanding answers. It was just this strange, heightened sensitivity she always experienced when dealing with him that made her so aware of it now. 'We were in the Louvre, Mrs Lawrence, Miss Jacobs, myself and the girls, when Catherine...well, Catherine just disappeared.'

'Nobody just disappears, Miss Marshall. She must have wandered off somewhere. Have you looked for her? Maybe she lost her way and even now is wondering where you all are!'

'Mr MacAllister, we spent two hours looking for her! We even enlisted the help of some of the guards on duty at the time. Believe me, she was nowhere to be found!' Perhaps she shouldn't have snapped at him like that, but did he have to make out that she was a complete fool? It was bad enough that Catherine should have gone missing, even worse what had transpired later, but to have him treat her like an imbecile... well!

'So she wasn't in the Louvre. Where else did you try? Have you been back to the hotel, Miss Marshall, or tried a few other places where she could have wandered off to looking for you? My daughter isn't the kind of girl who would go off on her own like that!'

'I doubt very much if you know what kind of a girl your daughter is, Mr MacAllister. Maybe that's the whole trouble!' She shouldn't have said that. Even as the words left her mouth Sarah regretted them, but it was too late to call them back. Her hand tightened on the receiver as she waited for his reaction, and she actually flinched when she heard the fury in his voice.

'Who the hell do you think you are, to make judgements like that? I pay that school where you work a lot of money to ensure my daughter gets a good education. What I don't expect is to have my relationship with Catherine commented on by a middle-aged spinster who doesn't know a thing about how a young girl's mind works!'

'How dare you? Mr MacAllister, I must object to——'

He cut her off, his voice harsh and unbending. 'Frankly, I don't give a damn what you object to, Miss Marshall. My only concern at present is my daughter and what has happened to her. I take it that you've informed the police?'

'Of course. However, in the circumstances, they suggested that I should wait a day or so before filing a missing persons report.'

'Circumstances? What circumstances? Catherine has disappeared, and I shall hold you solely responsible if anything happens to her because of your incompetence. Now I suggest that you get straight back on to the police and tell them I want her found now!'

'I think it might be better if you'd let me finish telling you what's happened, Mr MacAllister. Then decide what course of action we should take.' Sarah held on to her temper...just. 'I'm afraid Catherine's disappearance isn't quite what it seems. When I arrived back at the hotel earlier, I found a note in my room which she had left for me, a note informing me that she was going away with Philippe and that I wasn't to worry.'

'Philippe? Who's he? Just what are you trying to tell me, Miss Marshall?'

'Only that Catherine isn't lost, nor has she been abducted. She's run off with one of the waiters who work at the hotel. Now can you see why the police were reluctant to start a huge search for her? They told me that it isn't unusual for runaways to change their minds and come back of their own accord.'

'Run off? You're saying that you allowed my daughter to run off with some waiter while she was in your care? My God, woman, surely you must have had some idea what was happening? Couldn't you have taken steps to prevent it?'

'I'm afraid this has been as much a surprise to me as it is to you. I had no idea that Catherine was... that Catherine had spoken more than a few words to Philippe in the course of his duties.'

His anger was red-hot, sizzling down the line, scorching her, and she strove hard to restore some calm to the situation, but it was wasted effort. Nothing was going to cool James MacAllister's anger now, it seemed!

'You have eyes in your head, woman! You should have seen what was happening and stopped it! There aren't any excuses... none! Heaven knows that even with your background of academic purdah you should have seen the signs. You must have dealt with other fifteen-year-old girls who suddenly become infatuated, even though you might never have experienced such emotions yourself!'

The harsh words shouldn't have hurt. She should have ignored them, attributed them to his concern about his daughter, yet Sarah felt a sharp stab of pain. Was that how he and the rest of the world saw her, as an old maid locked away in an all-female environment, untouched by any normal emotions? Perhaps he was right at that; she had spent the last ten years hiding away from life, so it must have left its mark.

'... so I shall be there in a couple of hours' time.'

Sarah roused herself, suddenly aware that she'd missed part of what he'd said. 'I beg your pardon, but did you say that you were coming over here?'

'Of course. It's obvious that this mess needs to be sorted out, and just as obvious that you're incapable of doing it. I shall catch the first available flight.'

The sarcasm stung, but she bit back the sharp retort. 'And in the meantime do you want me to contact the police again?'

'Naturally. You might have that note, Miss Marshall, and I hope for your sake that it's genuine, but it doesn't change the fact that my daughter is missing. I want the police to find her and bring her back!'

'Catherine isn't a child. She's nearly sixteen.'

'I know how old she is. I also know that no power on earth is going to let me sit back while some young fellow with an eye to the main chance uses her!'

He slammed the receiver back down and cut the connection, and slowly Sarah followed suit, aware that she was shaking. She could understand his concern, but did he have to be so rude?

She closed her eyes, feeling the throbbing ache in her temples intensify. She had to compose herself before the rest of the party came back. They would have to be told, of course, but she wanted to keep it all as low-key as possible. If there had been any way of keeping it strictly between herself and James MacAllister that would have been better, but there was no hope of that. Poor Catherine was going to be the object of some unsavoury gossip when she got back to school—that was, if her father allowed her to return once this was over, which seemed doubtful. He seemed to think that this was all her fault, and maybe it was in a way. She had tried to warn him how unhappy Catherine was months ago, but he'd refused to listen. She should have tried harder to convince him, but would she have succeeded now that she knew what his true opinion of her was? A middle-aged spinster!

Sarah got up and went to the mirror hanging over the ornate fireplace, wanting to refute the cruel assessment, but there was little in the reflection to offer comfort. With her colourlessly pale skin, blue-grey eyes and light brown hair scraped back into a coil at the base of her neck she fitted the description almost too well, the perfect caricature of a spinsterish schoolma'am. Even her clothes were right for the part, the high-necked white blouse austerely plain against the dark navy cloth of her suit. Why had she never realised before how old she was starting to look, how severe? She glanced in the mirror each day, yet suddenly it shocked her that so many years must have passed since she'd seen a laughing face surrounded by a tumbling mass of curls smiling back. She had been such a different person then, happy, carefree, but then *it* had happened, and life had changed dramatically.

She turned away abruptly, blotting out the sharp, familiar pain. There was no going back, no changing what had happened, however much she might long to do so. Ten years ago she'd gathered up the broken threads and painfully woven them into what was her life today, and nothing could alter that.

The hotel was quiet now that the girls were all in bed. Sarah picked up the tiny cup of rich coffee that Madame had made for her and took a sip, enjoying the few minutes' peace and quiet after all the commotion. The girls had been agog once they had found out what had happened to Catherine. They had spent the evening speculating on where she was until Sarah could have screamed at them to stop. It was a relief when it was finally time for them to go to bed, and an even greater one when the other two teachers had decided to go up as well. She wasn't looking forward to the coming meeting with James MacAllister and would prefer it to go ahead without the presence of anyone else, especially if he chose to repeat his previous unflattering comments.

A car door slammed outside in the street and she put the cup down and sprang to her feet, feeling her heart leaping as she hurried to the window to look out. However, it wasn't Mr MacAllister, just another couple of guests who were staying at the hotel. Sarah went and sat back down in the chair, nodding politely to them as they made their way past the *salon* and called goodnight to her. Where was Mr MacAllister? He had told her that he was going to catch the first available flight, and that had been hours ago. If he'd been delayed then that was going to do little to improve his already nasty temper.

Sarah remained in the *salon* for another hour, but by the time the hall clock struck midnight she'd had enough. She was tired, worn out by the strain of the day, and the strain of coping with a dozen lively fifteen-year-olds for the past week. Whether James MacAllister was vexed or pleased, she had to get some sleep. She would leave a message with the night porter in case he arrived that she would see him in the morning.

Back in her room, she slipped off the suit jacket and hung it tidily on a hanger, then stripped off her skirt and blouse. She would have dearly loved a long hot bath, but the hotel didn't boast such luxuries as *en-suite* bathrooms, and she couldn't face the trek along the hall to the public bathroom at this time of the night. She would have to make do with a quick wash in the hand-basin.

She filled the basin, then started to soap her hands, murmuring in annoyance as a knock came at the door. Letting the soap slip into the basin, she looked round for her robe—then gasped in shock as the door was flung open and James MacAllister stepped into the room.

'Well, have you heard anything from Catherine yet?' He glared at her from the doorway, his dark eyes like ice as they skimmed her shocked face, and Sarah felt pure fear slide down her spine.

'Get out! What do you think you're doing barging in here like this? Get out at once!' She felt for the towel hanging on the rail by the basin, but it fell from her nerveless fingers.

'I'm not going anywhere, Miss Marshall.' He came into the room and closed the door, smiling as he saw her eyes widen. 'I'm sorry if I'm offending your sense of the proprieties, but now isn't the time to be concerned about modesty. Not with my daughter missing.'

'Catherine's disappearance doesn't give you the right to come walking into my room! Get out before I call the porter and have you thrown out! There's no excuse for this sort of behaviour, Mr MacAllister. It really is too much!'

'Too much? No, what's too much is the fact that you've allowed my daughter to run off with some French gigolo!' Fury set a rim of colour along his lean cheekbones, tightened his mouth into a thin hard line. Although he was leanly built there was an unmistakable strength to his body, an aura of physical power that was intimidating. His hair was very dark, almost black in the dim light from the overhead fitment, his skin deeply tanned, his eyes obsidian. He looked tough and uncompromising as he stood there glaring at her, and she felt her heart lurch sickeningly and hated herself for being afraid.

'No one *allowed* your daughter to run off. She *chose* to do so. And as for Philippe being a gigolo...!' She drew in an angry breath. 'Frankly, Mr MacAllister, you have no idea what you're talking about! However, I'm not prepared to discuss this further at present. I can understand your concern, but even that doesn't excuse such unpardonable behaviour. Please leave my room at once. We can continue this discussion in the *salon* when I'm dressed!'

'Frankly, Miss Marshall, I couldn't give a damn if you were stark naked! My only concern is Catherine, and if you think I'm going to delay our talk then think again. I've already wasted enough time, thanks to the vagaries of the French air traffic controllers who chose today to stage a work to rule.' He skimmed a glance over her, barely touching on her slim figure clad only in the sensible cotton bra and half-slip before he lifted the robe from behind the door and tossed it to her. 'Put this on if it makes you feel better, then maybe we can get down to discussing what's important rather than your affronted dignity!'

Sarah caught the robe and dragged it on, her face colouring at the note of scorn in his deep voice. Knotting the belt around her waist, she forced herself to meet his cold stare, willing the frantic beating of her heart to slow. Now that she was decently covered she felt marginally better, but she couldn't stop these sickening waves of anger and fear from coursing through her as she remembered the last time that a man had stood in her bedroom and faced her with anger in his eyes.

'Have you got that letter Catherine left for you?'

His voice cut into the darkness of her thoughts, bringing her abruptly back to the present. Without a word she turned towards the tall chest of drawers and picked up the note to hand it to him. He read it quickly, turning it over in his hand before looking at her from under lowered brows.

'And what did the police have to say about it? I take it you did remember to show it to them?'

Sarah ignored the stinging remark, drawing the lapels of the robe tighter around her throat, uncomfortable under the searching scrutiny. 'Naturally. However, they seemed to view it in a more positive light, a sign that we shouldn't worry too much, seeing that Catherine has gone willingly with Philippe.'

'Willingly? She's little more than a child! Too young to know what she's doing!' His face darkened with rage, his black eyes glittering with it, and Sarah took an instinctive step backwards. Even now the memories were stirring, those dark, bitter memories which she kept hidden deep inside her most of the time. Once she had lived with them day and night, lived and breathed the nightmare, but time had eased the fear until she'd been able to keep it locked at the very back of her mind. Now the rage on James MacAllister's face unlocked the door, letting the memories slide back slowly, insidiously, and she trembled with the sheer force of effort it took to hold them at bay.

'Mr MacAllister, this is getting us nowhere at all. I've told you what the police had to say, but that doesn't mean that I agree with them. Of course Catherine is too young to make a decision like this, but you have to appreciate their point of view. Philippe didn't abduct your daughter, she went willingly. That's obvious from the note.'

'Is it? You're a mind-reader, are you? You can tell what my daughter was thinking when she wrote this?' He flung the paper back at her, his face carved into grim lines as he took a step towards her, moving so close that Sarah could feel the heat radiating from his powerful body, smell the faint musky aroma of soap which clung to his skin, and she flinched away in an instinctive reaction he immediately saw.

'What the hell's the matter with you? You're as jumpy as a cat!' He reached out to touch her, his fingers hard and cool as they brushed her arm under the short sleeve of the robe, and Sarah backed away from him at once.

'Don't touch me!' She spat the order at him, her body tensing under the light touch of his hand on her arm. He stared at her in silence for a long moment, then let his hand drop to his side.

'Don't worry, I have no intention of touching you again. I shall save my concern for my daughter. She's the one who needs it!' He turned away, his shoulders hunched as he paced across the room and drew back the curtain to stare out of the window. 'Have you any idea what I'm going through, Miss Marshall? Do you even care, I wonder, or is Catherine's disappearance just an inconvenience in your tidy life, a hiccup in your careful schedule?'

'That's not fair. Of course I'm worried about her. Catherine is one of my best pupils.' She could breathe easier now that he had moved away, could subdue the panic that had threatened to claim her just now. She was a grown woman now, not a child of twenty, alone, confused, frightened. And whatever James MacAllister felt for her it wasn't lust!

'Your best pupil—how detached! Is that all she means to you, Miss Marshall? You surprise me. I had an idea from the way you've been handing out your opinions recently that Catherine was more than just a pupil, that you might in fact be concerned about her welfare!' The scorn was cold and hard on his face as he turned to look at her, and Sarah stiffened.

'Naturally I'm concerned. She's a very sweet girl, and recently I've had the feeling that she's been deeply unhappy about something or other. That's why I tried to talk to you at the last open day. Unfortunately, though, you chose to ignore my warnings, and now this has happened.'

'Oh, no, I'm not letting you get away with that, Miss Marshall.' He smiled tightly, his lips barely moving in a mere travesty of cold amusement which never touched his eyes.

'Get away with what?' Sarah could feel the tension humming and singing along her veins. If only he would leave, agree to wait until the morning to talk this through when she would feel better able to cope. She was far too tired and overwrought to follow what he meant.

'With shifting the blame on to me. Catherine was your responsibility while she was here. She was in your care when she disappeared. It was you who failed to see what was going on under your nose, and the blame is yours,

Miss Marshall, not mine. I entrusted her to your care, and you failed!'

'That's as untrue as it's unfair!' Sarah drew herself up, tossing her head to shake back a few long strands of hair which had come free from the coil. It incensed her that he should try to make her the scapegoat for his own shortcomings when she had tried so hard to warn him that there was something wrong months before. 'The only reason that Catherine has chosen a course of action totally alien to her nature is that she's been driven to it by your lack of attention, Mr MacAllister! How many times have you bothered to visit your daughter this past year? How many times have you spared the time to write her a letter from one of your frequent trips abroad? If anyone's to blame for Catherine's disappearance then it's you, with your insensitive behaviour!'

'I'm a very busy man, Miss Marshall. I have to make frequent trips abroad in the course of my work. Catherine understands that. One of the reasons I chose to send her to that school of yours is that my lifestyle is hardly conducive to providing her with a stable home life.'

Anger rippled through the deep tones, but this time Sarah didn't feel intimidated by it. It infuriated her that he should try to dismiss his responsibilities in such a way. 'Boarding school is hardly a substitute for a happy home life!' she retorted. 'I appreciate that it might be difficult for you, Mr MacAllister, as it is for many of our parents, but Catherine needs to know you're there if she needs you, that you care! You might be able to pay for her education, but you can't pay for the one thing *you* should be giving her—love!'

'You know nothing at all about my relationship with my daughter. She has always been extremely happy until this year when she fell under your influence. What ideas have you been planting in her head, I wonder? I had no trouble with Catherine until this past year, then suddenly all her letters are filled with things like "Miss Marshall says", or "when I was talking to Miss Marshall". Just what sort of a game have you been playing with my daughter? Why have you suddenly started to use your influence on how she thinks?' He paused, his face grim as he studied her for a long, silent minute, then when he spoke his voice was silky-smooth, like the throbbing, pulsating purr of a tiger before it made its kill. 'Could it be a way you've devised of getting through to me?'

'I...I have no idea what you mean.' She sounded breathless, uncertain, and he smiled slowly as he moved across the room to stand in front of her.

'Haven't you? I wonder why I suddenly find that hard to believe?' He laughed softly, watching the way her eyelids flickered before they fell to shield her eyes from that strangely disturbing scrutiny which seemed to lay her very soul bare. 'I accused you of being an emotionless spinster this morning, but maybe that was quite wrong.'

'I have no idea what you're talking about, Mr MacAllister, and, frankly, no desire to find out either! This is starting to verge on the ridiculous.' She tried to walk past him, but his hand closed around her upper arm, his fingers tightening just enough to stop her from getting away.

'Is it? Maybe, maybe not. Life's full of little surprises, Miss Marshall, as you must know. I must say the idea that you might be—how shall I put it?—attracted to me is a surprise all right.'

'Attracted to... No!' Sarah twisted her arm, suddenly desperate to break free from his hold, but he just drew her closer to him, a faint, mocking smile on his chiselled lips.

'No? Yet it could explain so much, couldn't it? The way you reacted at our last meeting, your insistence that I should have a private interview with you about Catherine when from my point of view there was nothing that needed to be said. When I think about it now, there's always been a certain tension when we've spoken, Miss Marshall. I always attributed it in the past to the fact that you had a deep-seated dislike of all men, but perhaps I was being obtuse in my assessment. Sexual awareness is a very strong emotion. It can produce the strangest symptoms in the most unlikely people.'

'No! How dare you? If there was tension when we met in the past then it probably stemmed from the fact that I dislike the way you treat your daughter!' She was desperate to convince him but, although his eyes glittered at her sharp words, the mocking smile stayed firmly in place.

'Is that so? Yet surely over the years you've been teaching there must have been other parents who you felt didn't give their children sufficient attention? Did you conduct interviews with them in the same tense manner, Miss Marshall? Did you bristle and exude such open animosity towards them too?' He shook his head as he met her widened eyes. 'I don't think so.'

'I don't care what you think, Mr MacAllister. How dare you come into my room and start accusing me of...of...?' She faltered, her face colouring as she tried to put his insinuations into words and failed. But he had none of her reluctance, it seemed.

'Making a play for me?' He raised one sleek black brow in polite enquiry, which didn't fool her a bit. There was nothing polite about James MacAllister, nothing remotely civilised. He was a dangerous man, and she'd been aware of that from the first time they'd met. Was that why she'd always been so tense when dealing with him, so aware of him? Probably. And somehow he had sensed it and was now interpreting her reaction in a way she had never intended.

She drew in a shuddery breath, forcing herself to meet those devil-dark eyes with a show of composure. 'I have not been making a play for you—far from it. I despise everything that you stand for, if you want the truth, despise the way you conduct your life without a thought for what it's doing to your daughter.'

'Is that a fact? I find it hard to believe when I weigh it all up. I'm not a vain man, Miss Marshall, but I am a realist. Women have chased me before for many reasons, not least of which being that as a fairly rich widower who isn't too bad-looking I fall into the "eligible" category. But I must admit to a certain surprise that you seem to have jumped on the bandwagon. I would never have placed you alongside them—but, of course, appearances can be so deceptive, don't you find? I had you neatly summed up as a prudish spinster when that seems to be far removed from the truth.'

His fingers tightened around her arm, biting into her flesh as he hauled her to him. 'I suppose I should feel flattered, but right now I'm more concerned with what's happened to Catherine. So let's get this out of the way here and now, shall we?'

'What do you mean? Look, this is... Oh!' Sarah got no further; the words stopped on her lips as he bent his head and kissed her hard. There was a moment, one infinitesimal second when she went quite still, enthralled by the unfamiliar feel of his hard mouth on hers, then the nightmare broke through the barriers in her mind and she started to struggle wildly, beating his shoulders with her clenched fists before raking her nails down the side of his face.

He swore roughly as her nails gouged his skin and thrust her away, his face dark with fury, but she was beyond the bounds of reason now, beyond caring what he thought.

'Get out!' Her voice was hoarse, rasping, echoing round the silence that filled the room.

'I'm going. But this isn't finished yet, Sarah Marshall.' He ran a hand down his cheek, wiping away a trace of blood, his eyes pinning her where she stood shaking in front of him. 'Nobody normal reacts like that. I won't forget this, believe me. You, lady, have problems, and I'm going to make certain that once I have Catherine safely back again you don't get the chance to influence any other susceptible young minds. I'm going to make it my business to see that you never teach any child again!'

He turned and walked from the room, slamming the door behind him. Sarah watched him go, her whole body shaking in reaction to what had happened and what he'd said afterwards. What would she do if he carried out his threat, and she couldn't find sanctuary in teaching? She dreaded to think. Her job had been her salvation over the years, the one thing that had held her together. Without that she'd have nothing. He said she had problems, and he was right, disturbingly so, but the biggest problem she now had, it seemed, was James MacAllister himself!

CHAPTER TWO

SUNLIGHT reflected off the puddles on the flagstoned terrace. Sarah rested her head back against the chair and closed her eyes, feeling the tiredness in every cell of her body. Not surprisingly she'd hardly slept, and her head was heavy, her eyes burning so that the reflected glare from the May sun hurt. All night long she'd lain stiffly in the bed praying for morning to come, but now it had it offered no release from the nightmare which still lived and breathed inside her. Now there were new images and fresh scenes to add to all the others that had haunted her for so long, stilted pictures of her and James MacAllister: the expression on his face when he'd confronted her in the bedroom, the cold, hard mockery in his eyes when he'd hauled her to him and kissed her, then, last and worst, the sheer magnitude of his anger as he'd stood wiping the blood from his face. It might be morning and the night had fled, but it was far from over.

'Sarah? Are you all right?'

She jumped violently, smoothing her face into less tortured lines as she turned towards the door and saw Stephanie Jacobs, one of the other teachers, standing there watching her with concern.

'Yes, I'm fine, thank you. Just a little tired, that's all. I didn't sleep too well worrying about Catherine.' The lie slid so easily off her tongue that she felt almost guilty, but how could she explain the truth of what had kept her awake? How could she explain that James MacAllister had openly accused her of making a play for him, then kissed her, and that she, instead of dealing with it rationally, had reacted like a madwoman? No one knew about her past and she never intended that they should know. Yet there was no way she could confide in Stephanie without telling her everything to put the incident in context.

'I know what you mean. I can't stop worrying about her too. Do you think she'll come to her senses and realise what a silly thing she's done once she's had time to think it through?' Stephanie's pretty face was filled with concern. 'I can't understand why she should do such a thing, Sarah. She's always been such a quiet girl!'

Sarah smiled sadly. 'I'm rather afraid that could be the trouble. Catherine's too quiet. She keeps everything inside her instead of talking about what's worrying her. I sensed there was something wrong a few months ago, but I never dreamt she'd do anything like this. I had hoped she'd come to me eventually and tell me what was wrong, then maybe we could have worked it out. I feel I'm responsible for what's happened now.'

'Don't blame yourself! If anyone's at fault it's that father of hers. She idolises him! Honestly, Sarah, it makes me sick the way some parents dump their children in school and then barely spare them a second thought!'

Stephanie's face was pink with indignation, which Sarah could sympathise with. She agreed with every word the younger woman said. If anyone was to blame for Catherine's actions it was her father—not that he would accept that, of course. He had to have a scapegoat to appease his conscience, and it seemed that role had fallen to her!

'I doubt if he'd agree with your assessment, Steph. I tried telling him I was worried a few months ago, but he refused to listen. More interested in his own life, his own concerns, than what was happening to his daughter!' There was condemnation in Sarah's voice as she responded to the wholly justified criticism. In her view, James MacAllister had shirked his responsibilities, and now Catherine was paying the price for his lack of concern.

'I resent you making observations like that, Miss Marshall. My daughter is very important to me, and I have no intention of allowing you or anyone else to state differently.'

There was anger in the deep voice that cut into their conversation, an echo of what she'd witnessed the previous night. Sarah felt the blood swell and pound along her veins as she looked round to see James MacAllister standing at the end of the terrace. Just for a moment the memories swam into her mind, filling her head, before she ruthlessly suppressed them. Last night was over and she might not be able to change what had happened, but she had to learn to cope with it if she was to get through the day. Until Catherine was found she would have to find the strength to deal with her father without falling apart. It just surprised her somewhat that she should choose a way that was guaranteed to annoy him even more.

'Is she? Really important to you, Mr MacAllister? Then I must apologise for what I said.' She smiled with a cold sweetness. 'However, I do wonder exactly where she fits into your list of priorities, being so very important to you.'

'I beg your pardon?' He moved along the terrace, dark and dangerous-looking in black jeans and an open-necked black knit shirt which clung to the muscular lines of his lean body as he stood towering over her. 'Would you be good enough to explain that?'

'I shouldn't have thought it needed explaining—but if you insist.' She met his eyes for a moment, then lowered her head to escape the coldness of the black stare, smoothing her hand over the lapels of her neat white blouse and down the pleats of her grey skirt. 'Everyone has a list of priorities in his life—home, family, job. You're a very successful businessman with interests world-wide. I just wondered in what order you'd place your concern for Catherine . . . before or after your business?'

Maybe if her head hadn't been aching and her body humming with tension and she hadn't spent one of the most miserable nights of her life awake because of him, she might have found a different, more tactful way of phrasing it. Maybe. But she doubted it. This man had mocked her, frightened her, opened up the floodgates, and now all the hurt and resentment came spilling out.

'Catherine's welfare has always been my number one priority. There's no question of me ever putting her second. None!' He was coldly furious now, his eyes narrowed to glittering slits, his jaw tight, and Stephanie murmured some hasty excuse and hurried away. Sarah barely noticed her leaving as all the pain and anguish erupted inside her into a fury equal to his.

'Never? Forgive me for sounding sceptical, but what about her birthday? Did you remember it, send a card to her, or a present?' She shook her head, her pale skin touched with colour, her eyes a deep stormy grey. 'Catherine haunted the school office all day waiting for a message to come, a card, anything, but it didn't, because you were too busy with your own interests to remember something as insignificant as your daughter's fifteenth birthday!'

'I was in Bolivia, miles away from the nearest town. There was no way I could pop out and buy her a card! I explained that to her when I got back.'

'And that was supposed to make up for the disappointment, was it? An explanation that you couldn't get to a shop? You didn't see her that day, Mr MacAllister, but I did. I saw how upset she was, saw how she tried to make light of the fact that you'd forgotten in front of her friends. And yet you still insist that you put Catherine first in your life!'

She stood up, gathering up the cardigan she'd left draped over the back of the chair to walk back inside, too annoyed to trust herself to stay a moment longer. However, he stepped in front of her and barred her way.

'I don't insist on anything. Whether you choose to believe me or not doesn't concern me, Miss Marshall. What does concern me is the fact that you've been planting such ideas in Catherine's head.'

'Planting ideas...now look here, that's just not so! I've never said one word, not one, that could be construed as criticism of your behaviour. I'm not so insensitive as to do that.' She glared up at him, having to tilt her head so that she could look him in the eye, then immediately regretted it when she saw the chilling coldness in those dark depths. 'Catherine worships the ground you walk on, Mr MacAllister. That's the trouble. If she could only see you for what you are then maybe she could put your behaviour into perspective and face the fact that her father isn't Prince Charming and Superman all rolled into one!'

'And what am I really?' He smiled, his thin, chiselled lips drawing back from strong white teeth in an expression which held more menace than amusement. 'Come along, Miss Marshall, don't stop there, not when this is just starting to get interesting. You say that Catherine should see me for what I really am, so what exactly is that? How do you see me, in fact?'

It was tempting, so very tempting, but Sarah managed to hold on to the last vestiges of control. 'My opinion doesn't matter a jot. It's how your daughter sees you that's important.'

'So you finally accept that, do you? That it's Catherine's opinion that matters, not yours?' His eyes skimmed her softly flushed face, lingering for a heartbeat on the unadorned curve of her full lower lip. 'Then maybe putting up with your behaviour last night was worth it if it achieved that much.'

'I don't know what you mean.' She tried to step around him, but he moved sideways and blocked her path again, folding his arms across his chest as he studied her in silence for a long moment.

'You aren't a convincing liar, Miss Marshall. You know exactly what I mean all right. I haven't forgotten what happened and how you attacked me like a madwoman.'

'Me? *I* attacked *you*? Oh, come on!' Fury rose inside her and she rounded on him. 'You were the one who...who...' Why should it be so hard to get a simple word out, to state clearly and calmly that he had been the one to start things by *kissing* her? Sarah fought a silent inner battle then gave it up as she saw the cruel mockery sparkling in his eyes. Her head came up and she stared back at him, refusing to give an inch. 'You were the one who attacked me last night. You came into my room, uninvited, abused me verbally and then resorted to physical violence. I could, if I were so inclined, bring charges against you for that.'

'Could you indeed? I doubt if they'd stick, especially when people saw the evidence of your handiwork.' He turned his face, and Sarah felt sickness well inside her as she saw the angry scratches running from the side of his ear to the curve of his strong jaw.

'It was your own fault. You shouldn't have said what you did, nor tried to kiss me like that.' Her voice was low, ashamed, and he gave her a speculative look.

'Maybe not, but you must admit that I had provocation. I was, and still am, sick with worry about Catherine, and to my mind you're more than partly to blame for planting ideas in her head, for whatever reason you may have done so.'

'I haven't! Why won't you try to see sense? I've never tried to influence Catherine in any way, and especially not so that I could...could make a play for you! Frankly, Mr Marshall, I can live quite happily without male companionship, so don't kid yourself into thinking I've ever had any designs on you!'

'That's what you say now, but of course you would. You're hardly going to admit what you'd planned now that it's all backfired.' He shook his head, sunlight glinting on the silvery wings at his temples which only served to highlight the night-darkness of the rest. 'But there's no way I'm letting you get away with what you've done. Catherine was a perfectly happy, well-adjusted child until she fell under your influence. She would never have done such a stupid, reckless thing as running off unless someone had put the idea into her head.'

'I beg your pardon? You're actually accusing me of giving her the idea to do that! Come on, Mr MacAllister, even you can't be so stupid as to think that! First I'm supposed to have had designs on you, then I've been influencing your daughter to run off? You're mad! The last thing I want is for anything to happen to Catherine, irrespective of how I feel about you!'

'Then how do you explain her actions? You claim to know my daughter, so you tell me why she's done this.'

What was it in his voice which made the anger fade abruptly? Was it just the pain she could hear in those deep tones? Sarah couldn't decide. All she knew was that whereas moments before she would have given anything to watch James MacAllister suffer, now she wanted to ease his pain just as much.

'I don't think it's that easy,' she told him. 'I imagine that Catherine's motives are so mixed up that we'd need her to explain them to us.'

'But she must have known how worried I'd be. Doesn't that count for anything? Damn it all, I'd do anything in the world for that child, and she knows it...she knows it!'

'Does she?' Sarah's voice was gentle as she tried to soothe the pain she could sense tearing him apart. She might not agree with how he had treated his daughter, but there was no denying that his concern was genuine, the grief he felt very real, and grief was an emotion she had grown to know very well over the past years.

'Of course she does. She must! Everything I do is for her, to give her a better life and secure her future.' He turned away, gripping the rail which fenced off the terrace until his knuckles gleamed through the skin. 'It isn't easy bringing up a child alone, especially not a daughter. When...when my wife died I thought long and hard about what I should do for the best before deciding that Catherine would be better off at boarding-school so that she would have some stability in her life.

'I have to travel a good deal in my work, and I didn't want to leave her with a series of housekeepers. It seemed the ideal solution, especially when she seemed quite happy to go along with the plan. Now you're telling me that what I thought was for the best was, in fact, wrong?' He turned and faced her then, his face hard and uncompromising in the glare of the sun. 'I can't accept that, Miss Marshall. I shall never accept that, in fact!'

Despite the warmth of the sun, Sarah shivered. Quickly she drew the cardigan around her shoulders, clinging hold of the soft, warm wool. 'I never said it was wrong to send Catherine away to school. She's been very happy with us until fairly recently.'

'Until she came under your unsettling influence, to be precise.' He straightened abruptly, towering over her so that she took a quick step back, suddenly frighteningly conscious of the last time he had stared at her with such anger on his face.

He must have read her mind, because he smiled tautly, his face grim. 'Oh, you don't need to worry. I'm not fool enough to repeat my mistakes.' He ran a hand down the livid marks on his cheek, holding her gaze until colour stained her throat and face. 'You can say what you like, Miss Marshall, make any amount of protestations, but nothing will change my mind as to where the responsibility lies. Once I've found Catherine then I'm going to make certain that I carry out my promise and ensure that no other child falls under your influence, and that no other parent goes through what I'm suffering. You'll never teach again, Miss Marshall, I can guarantee that!'

He walked past her without another word, leaving her shaking. He meant every word, meant to take the one thing she had in life away from her, and it seemed that she was powerless to stop him. A moan escaped from her lips and she pressed a hand to her mouth, terrified that if she gave in now she would quickly fall apart. Life had taught her to fight for what she wanted, and she had done it before, overcome all obstacles until she'd finally reached her goal. Now she had to find the strength to fight again, only this time the opponent wouldn't be inside her head but a real live person. Whatever happened, she had to find the strength to fight James MacAllister and convince him that what he was planning was wrong.

'Has he gone? Wow, Sarah, I don't think I've ever seen anyone so furious before! I don't know how you had the nerve to stand up to him!'

Stephanie came out on to the terrace, her pretty face filled with a comforting mixture of awe and admiration as she looked at Sarah. Sarah forced a shaky smile, using the mantle of calm she'd developed over the years to hide her true feelings from the younger woman. 'I think he knows deep down that he's partly to blame. That's probably why he's so angry. It must be hard for a man with Mr MacAllister's ego to accept he could be wrong.'

Stephanie laughed, some of the tension leaving her as she heard Sarah's comment. 'Trust you to think of that! I wish I could understand people as well as you do.'

The compliment was genuine, but was it valid? Did she understand people? A day or so ago she might have agreed, but after the run-ins she'd had recently with James MacAllister she hesitated. James MacAllister was a law unto himself, and no one would ever fully understand how his mind worked unless he wanted them to. It made the task of convincing him how wrong he was to try to ruin her career that much more difficult.

'It's all part of the job, Stephanie,' she said noncommittally.

'Mmm, and the part I dislike most.' Stephanie shrugged when she caught Sarah's startled look. 'Does that sound very disillusioned? Because that's the way I feel—disillusioned with the whole idea of teaching.' She walked over to stare out through the trees which separated the terrace from the bustle of the narrow street. 'I don't think I'm going to stay in this job much longer, Sarah, if you want the truth. I was starting to feel restless before this trip, but now...'

She grinned suddenly, spreading her arms wide. 'Paris, Sarah, the centre of the civilised world! Doesn't it make you want to throw it all up and see more of the world, live a little before you get too old to enjoy yourself? There's a lot of life out there, and I don't intend to spend the rest of mine teaching girls who haven't the least inclination to know where Mount Kilimanjaro is, or how igneous rock was formed!'

Sarah laughed almost bitterly. 'I think I'm past that. My idea of a good life is staying exactly how I am and continuing with teaching.'

'Past it? Oh, come on! We were only talking about you the other day in the staffroom.' She saw Sarah's expression and had the grace to blush. 'I know, I know, but it's only natural that people should be curious. You're—what, thirty…thirty-one? Yet you seem to have no life outside school. Why, Sarah? Why should you want to bury yourself in that place? You're only young yet, but if you don't do something soon life will have passed you by.'

'I like my life exactly as it is, thank you, so don't worry about me. Now, have you got the itinerary sorted out for the day? It was Notre Dame on the agenda, if I'm not mistaken.'

Stephanie sighed, not at all abashed by Sarah's attempts to change the subject. 'You're never mistaken, Sarah—that's the whole trouble. You should have a lot of other things to think about apart from the itinerary!'

'Maybe, but I'm afraid I see this trip as my responsibility.' There was a touch of ice in Sarah's voice as she replied, but it failed to freeze the shock which ran through her system when James MacAllister spoke from directly behind her.

'I'm glad to hear it. That should make things a whole lot simpler over the next few days if you keep in mind that this trip, and everything that's happened on it, is your responsibility.'

Sarah turned to look at him, schooling her face into an expression of polite enquiry, but she couldn't teach her muscles to relax, her whole body to lose the tension which invaded her limbs. 'Why do I have the feeling that there's a point to that observation, Mr MacAllister?' she asked.

'Probably because there is one.' He stepped out on to the terrace, but stopped just by the door so that she would have no chance to go back inside unless he chose to allow it. 'I've just been talking to Madame Sicot. She informed me that Philippe isn't from Paris. He comes from a small town near the Spanish border. Evidently he's the son of a distant relative of hers, and she only gave him the job as a favour.'

'I see. Interesting as this is, Mr MacAllister, is there a point to this story?' Sarah glanced at her watch, feeling tension singing along her veins. He was up to something, she just knew it, knew that he was about to tell her something she wouldn't want to hear, yet she felt powerless to stop the events from unfolding one by one.

'Naturally. I wouldn't be wasting time if there weren't, not when it's my daughter who's missing.' He folded his arms across his chest as he leant against the door-frame and studied her with a barely veiled hostility. 'Evidently Philippe has been feeling homesick in the city. He'd discussed returning to his village with a couple of the other waiters, and they're convinced that's where he's gone, taking Catherine with him.'

'I see. Then the police should be informed.'

'I have every intention of phoning them. However...' he shrugged eloquently '...I'm not prepared to sit here waiting to see what happens. Finding Catherine is down to us as far as I'm concerned now.'

'Us? What do you mean?' The net was closing now, she could sense it, sense that she was being drawn further and further into something she wasn't going to like.

'It's quite simple. I want my daughter back as soon as possible, before that young fellow has a chance to do any more damage. That being so, I intend to follow her and Philippe back to his home, and you, Miss Marshall, are coming with me.'

'Me? I... But... No! That's the most ridiculous thing I've ever heard. I can't come with you. I have the rest of the girls to think about. They can't be left.'

He smiled grimly, his face cold and determined in the clear, sharp light. 'I thought you'd say that, so I took the liberty of telephoning the school and speaking to your headmistress. She's sending another member of staff over on the first available flight to free you to accompany me. She feels that in the circumstances it's your duty to go with me. In fact, she went so far as to assure me that that would be what you would want to do. So get your things packed, Miss Marshall. We leave in half an hour.' He turned to go back inside, then paused and glanced back over his shoulder. 'Look on this as a second chance. If you come up to scratch and help me get Catherine back then maybe I can be persuaded to reconsider my decision about your future in teaching.'

He disappeared inside the hotel, leaving Sarah staring after him with panic in her eyes. She wanted to run after him and tell him that she wouldn't go with him, but how could she? If she crossed him now she wasn't fool enough to imagine that he would let the matter drop. James MacAllister was an influential man; he knew people in many high places. If he chose he could ruin her reputation and no school would employ her in the future. Yet how could she cope with the thought of accompanying him on this desperate search across France? How?

CHAPTER THREE

THE pavement was dry, but the air still held that washed-clean fragrance which a few hours of heavy city traffic would soon dispel. Sarah carried her case out to the steps and stopped for a moment, drinking in the scent of Paris in the spring. On a sudden impulse, she closed her eyes and let her mind spin back in time to when she had been a student and spent a year studying at the Sorbonne. It had been a wonderful time, the most wonderful in her whole life; golden days when the world had lain at her feet, her life waiting ahead of her like a huge adventure. It made what had come next so much worse just by comparison. If she could turn back the clock then she would turn it back to that time and hold it there forever.

'Are you going to stand there all day daydreaming? We've wasted enough time as it is without you wasting any more. Come on!'

The curt command brought her abruptly out of her reverie and Sarah looked towards the road, her heart lurching when she saw James MacAllister standing next to a sleek black car with his hands on his hips and annoyance all over his face. Just for a moment terror held her immobile, then she drew in a calming breath and struggled the case down the steps. She had telephoned the school and spoken to her headmistress before she'd started to pack, hoping to find some way to convince her that this whole plan was crazy, but Mrs Hunt had been adamant that it was the only course of action in the circumstances. She had been uncharacteristically sharp, leaving Sarah with the distinct impression that she held her to blame for Catherine's disappearance. No doubt James MacAllister had been behind that view. It was so unfair, but Sarah had known there would be little point in protesting. Mrs Hunt was only concerned with the school's reputation, and if there was a way of getting Catherine back safely while keeping the whole incident quiet then that must be of primary importance. Sarah's feelings counted for nothing.

'What the hell have you got in there? Armour?' James MacAllister hefted the case into the boot and slammed the lid, glaring coldly at her, but Sarah ignored him. She'd made up her mind to stay calm throughout this trip and not allow that crazy, wild anger she'd experienced last night and earlier this morning to surface again. It was the only way she would survive.

'Obviously I need a change of clothes in case we're away overnight. It could take that long to find Catherine.' She slid into the seat and smoothed her pleated skirt over her knees with a composure which didn't betray her annoyance at his comment.

He got in beside her and started the engine, then slipped the car into gear to pull out into the traffic. 'It could take far longer than that, so resign yourself to that from the outset. We have several hundred miles to cover and some rough roads once we get into the mountains.'

'Then wouldn't it make sense to fly to Toulouse and start the search from there? We'd be closer to Philippe's home. This seems like a great waste of time to me when we have no real idea of which route they've taken, or even if they're heading straight there at all.'

He shook his head, his eyes centred on the road as they moved out from the side-street into the fast flow of the city traffic. 'No, it isn't a waste of time.' He lifted a crumpled map from the dashboard and tossed it to her, his eyes skimming her set face. 'One of the waiters gave me this. He found it in Philippe's room. Take a look at it and see if you recognise the handwriting.'

Sarah glanced down at the map, studying the notes made in the narrow margin before glancing uncertainly back at him. 'It looks like Catherine's writing, but I can't be sure.'

'It is her writing. Obviously she helped plan the route, but do you have any idea exactly how they intend to travel all those hundreds of miles?' There was such cold anger in the dark, deep tones that involuntarily Sarah shivered.

'Not really. By car?'

He laughed harshly. 'No. Philippe is the proud owner of an old motorbike which he's been doing up for the past few months, and apparently they intend to make the journey on that. From what I gather there isn't much chance of it making it that far, so now do you see why I'm not prepared to simply fly there and wait for them to arrive? Anything could happen along the way. God, it's bad enough that she's gone off with some guy she barely knows, but on a motorbike that's held together more by will-power... ! Anything could happen to her, any damned thing at all! I wouldn't put it past that fellow to dump her if they broke down and she became an inconvenience to him.'

'I don't think that would happen. Philippe seemed . . . well, he seemed like a nice quiet sort of a boy on the few occasions I spoke to him. I'm sure he'll look after Catherine.'

'Now that does ease my mind, Miss Marshall. Thank you for the glowing reference. I shall rest easier from now on knowing that the man who made off with my daughter has your approval!'

Sarah's face coloured and she forgot her plan to remain calm at all times. 'There's no need to be sarcastic! The very least you could do, seeing that you've press-ganged me into accompanying you, is to be polite, otherwise you can stop and let me out right here. I don't intend to bear the brunt of your ill temper for the next few days!'

'You, Miss Marshall, will have to put up with whatever I decide to dish out. You aren't in a position to demand anything. If you'd done your job properly in the first place and kept control of the situation then none of this would ever have happened! So being polite and sparing your feelings is way down my list of priorities!'

'I've always done my job properly, and I resent you saying otherwise. Don't forget that I was the one who tried to warn you something was wrong with Catherine, but you chose to ignore that warning!'

'So we're back to that, are we? You tried to warn me... Tried to warn me about what? That in your opinion Catherine was unhappy?' He took his eyes from the road, his gaze tangling disturbingly with hers for a moment. 'I don't remember you making much sense. You seemed to be more concerned with criticising my lifestyle than in voicing your concerns about Catherine. And you most definitely didn't mention anything along the lines of her running off. If you'd been doing your job properly, my dear Miss Marshall, then you would have managed to tell me more than some rambling tirade about her being unhappy and it being my fault!'

'But it is your fault! Can't you see that Catherine has done this because your lack of attention has driven her to it?'

'No, I damned well can't! I didn't drive her into doing anything so stupid, but I know who has. I know who first planted the idea in her head, and, believe me, you won't get away with it!'

What had she expected? That he would have come to his senses and realised he was wrong? No way. The day that James Almighty MacAllister ever admitted he could be at fault was the day that hell froze over!

They drove on in silence, not a comfortable silence but one that seethed with bad feelings and an anger so real that the air seemed charged with emotion. It made Sarah feel on edge, her whole body tense. Deliberately, she tried to relax, resting her head back against the seat as she watched Paris whirl by in a haze of speeding traffic. Parisian drivers were renowned for their erratic behaviour, but James MacAllister seemed unfazed by it as he drove the car with a steady confidence across the city until he reached the main route towards Orléans. Just for a second he glanced her way, and Sarah turned her head and met his eyes before turning away, feeling her breath tight in her chest as the car picked up speed, leaving Paris behind. Now they were truly on their way, just her and this man who seemed to unleash so many strange emotions inside her which she'd never experienced before. Something told her that her life would never be the same once this journey was over, and the thought frightened her, frightened her almost as much as her reaction to James MacAllister did. She didn't want anything to rock her safe little world. She didn't want to be forced to leave the sanctuary she had built for herself, but little by little she could sense the foundations crumbling away, leaving her vulnerable once more.

Her neck ached, the muscles stiff from lying in the one position for so long. Sarah groaned softly and moved her head, wondering why the pillow felt so hard under her cheek. She opened her eyes and blinked, then felt awareness come flooding back. She sat bolt upright, running a hand over her dishevelled hair, looking anywhere but at the man whose shoulder she had been lying on.

'I thought you were going to sleep all afternoon. I'm hungry, so let's go inside and get something to eat.'

He barely spared her a glance as he opened the car door and stepped out. He obviously wasn't at all bothered about having her use his shoulder as a pillow, but she was. She felt hot with embarrassment at having woken to find herself curled against him like that. It had been so...so intimate.

Her blood heated at the thought of how she'd slept on his shoulder, and she turned away as he looked back at the car, making a great performance out of pinning her hair back into its smooth, neat coil, but her hands were shaking so hard that all she managed to do was dislodge even more hairpins.

'For heaven's sake, woman! We don't have time for you to start on the routine of pinning your hair back into that bun. Here, I can soon sort you out.' He came back and reached inside the car to haul her across the seat while he pulled the rest of the restraining pins out. Quickly he ran his fingers through the thick shining mass of hair, then straightened and viewed her dispassionately for a moment. 'That will do fine. Looks a damned sight better than it usually does, in fact. Now, do you think we can get on with having something to eat at last? I want to make it to Limoges before evening so we can look round in case Catherine is there, as it's one of the stops on her route, but if you keep up this dilly-dallying then we'll be lucky to get out of Châteauroux before nightfall!'

He pulled the keys from the ignition, then slammed and locked the car door before setting off towards the small roadside café. Sarah stared after him in something akin to shock. Tentatively she ran a hand over her tumbled hair, then felt the anger start to grow inside her once more. How dared he do that, have the sheer audacity to snatch the pins out of her hair like that?

Furious, she pulled down the sun-visor and stared angrily at her reflection in the small vanity mirror, wondering how best to restrain the wild tangle of curls when all the pins were gone, then stopped and frowned. She looked so different like this, with her soft brown hair framing her face in silken curls which fell past her shoulders. Somehow it seemed to soften the thin lines of her face and make her eyes look even larger than they were. Just for a moment she had the funniest feeling that time had slipped back to those years when she'd been a student. She had always worn her hair long and carefree like this then, a reflection of how she had felt herself. What a long time it had been since she'd felt that way, it seemed.

She touched a soft brown curl with her fingertip, then abruptly snatched her hand away as she realised what a fool she was being. She wasn't that young girl now but a mature and sensible woman, a woman who wouldn't dream of going into a public place looking as though she had just got out of bed. That James MacAllister had said she looked better like this was reason enough to remedy his handiwork at once!

Opening her bag, she searched through the contents until she found a thick rubber band and quickly pulled her hair back and fastened it as neatly as she could into a ponytail. It wasn't a style she usually favoured, but it was the best she could do with such limited facilities. Opening the car door, she got out and walked up the path to the café, pausing for a moment as she let her eyes adjust to the dimness after the bright glare of the sun.

James MacAllister was sitting at a table near the window, nursing a cup of coffee between his hands. He glanced up as she pulled back a chair and joined him at the table, his eyes skimming over her hair, and defiantly Sarah tilted her head, daring him to pass some comment. However, he said nothing as he slid the menu across the table, then turned away to look out of the window, and she experienced a strange little feeling of pique and wondered at it. Just for a moment she watched him, then she forced herself to turn her attention to the menu, but it seemed strangely difficult to concentrate on the selection of dishes. Her gaze would keep on sliding back to James MacAllister, her eyes lingering on his clean-cut profile, the way the thick black hair with those touches of silver at each temple waved almost to his collar, drawing attention to the strong column of his neck.

How old was he? Late thirties? Early forties? Catherine was almost sixteen, so logically he must be somewhere around that, but there was no softening to the hard lines of his face, no hint of weakness in the lean strength of his powerful body. He looked fit and virile, a man in his prime; an attractive, disturbing man who affected her far more than he should. She'd come into contact with other attractive men, parents of her pupils, yet none of them had had this unsettling effect on her that James MacAllister had.

'I suggest that you decide what you want to eat. We shall be setting off again within half an hour, so it will be your own fault if you haven't finished your meal. And for your information, Miss Marshall, I am *not* on the menu.'

She jumped when he spoke, her eyes lifting guiltily to his face, then felt hot embarrassment settle a fiery glow into her cheeks when she saw the mockery in his eyes. 'You'd probably give me indigestion even if you were. I'm sure you'd be far too tough for my palate, Mr MacAllister!'

Why on earth had she said that? She should have responded with some cold disclaimer, not virtually admitted that she *had* been sitting there watching him! The embarrassment doubled until she felt she would melt from the searing heat, but surprisingly he just laughed, his deep voice holding a note which sent a shiver coursing through her despite the heat in her veins.

'Maybe I'm just tough on the outside. Isn't it possible that I might have a soft centre? Want to find out... Sarah?'

'I... no! Of course not. And I would prefer it if you called me by my proper title.'

'Why?' He leant forward, resting his forearms on the plain white cloth as he studied her levelly. Sarah held the gaze for a moment, then hurriedly looked away, wondering why she felt so breathless. Her eyes dropped to his arms, the tanned flesh lightly covered with dark hair a startling contrast to the white cloth, and she swallowed hard, trying to ease the sudden tightness in her throat. What was the matter with her? Why was she acting like... like a teenager with a crush?

The thought alarmed her so much that her eyes flew up and she met the dark intensity of his gaze from the space of mere inches. Just for a moment time seemed to stop, holding them suspended in some place where no one else could enter. Then he smiled slowly, his mouth curling as he repeated the question.

'Why shouldn't I call you by your Christian name, Sarah?'

'Because I don't want you to.' It sounded silly even to her own ears, her voice thready, almost breathless, and she sensed rather than saw the amusement which rippled through him. It brought her up short, rid her head of those silly ideas which had filled it for one dangerous moment. She sat up straighter, unconsciously settling her features into the coolly restrained lines she used so often to distance herself from others.

'Because, *Mr* MacAllister, I much prefer to keep our...association on a purely business footing. There's no way that we can ever be anything more than mere acquaintances who, through circumstance, are forced to suffer one another's company. There's no point in adopting familiar terms as far as I can see.'

'No?' He sat back in his seat, one sleek dark brow quirking attractively as he frowned at her in mock-confusion. 'But don't you think it would be easier all round if we tried to get along? After all, Sarah, we shall be spending a lot of time together over the next week, so it seems petty to keep on like this.'

'It isn't petty. It's just common sense. Any time we spend together is purely in the interest of finding your daughter!'

Was that a touch of desperation in her voice? She hoped not, hoped even more that *he* wouldn't think so. She couldn't afford to weaken in this man's company. He was well versed in the art of dealing with women, far more versed than she would ever be in dealing with men!

'Oh, I'm not denying that our association is purely a business one,' he said. 'All I'm suggesting is that we try to make it as smooth and comfortable as possible. After all, we shall be spending several days...and several nights together.'

It wasn't what he said so much as the way he said it in that slow, deep voice which sent a shudder rippling through her. Sarah stilled, her whole body growing tense as she waited for the fear such words should evoke to rise, but she felt nothing like that, nothing but a deep thrill of excitement which made her whole body tingle.

It shocked her so much that she pushed the chair back from the table and stood up abruptly, her face ashen as she stared down at him.

'I don't know what you're playing at, but let me make it clear here and now that we won't be spending any nights together in that sense!'

He smiled almost cruelly, his eyes like black ice as he studied her face. 'You exhibit the strangest reactions, Sarah. I sometimes get the feeling that your head is saying one thing while your body is giving out an entirely different message altogether.'

'I have no idea what you mean.' She went to pick up her bag, but he caught her wrist, his long fingers locking around the slender delicate bones.

'Oh, I think you have. I think you have a very good idea what I'm talking about, and that's why you're so scared. Does it frighten your puritanical little mind that you can feel this way? That you can actually want a man physically despite the fact that you've deliberately chosen to live a life which excludes all men?'

'No! You...you have no idea what you're talking about. Let me go! I don't want anything to eat. I'll wait in the car.'

She twisted her arm to break his grip, but his fingers just fastened tighter around her wrist, holding her firmly though not harshly in place. 'You can't always run away from the truth, Sarah. Sometimes it won't be denied. It has to find an outlet one way or another, and this is a prime example of how dangerous it can be to bury your head in the sand.' He pulled her closer so that he could stare into her face. 'If you'd admitted to yourself how you felt then maybe none of this would ever have happened and Catherine wouldn't now be living out your fantasies.'

'I...' She stared at him in horror, scarcely able to comprehend what he was saying.

'I see you understand at last, don't you? It was you who put this idea of running off into my daughter's head, wasn't it? Oh, don't try and lie, to me or to yourself, any longer. I've seen instances of this before—frustration finding its outlet. What did you do? Fill her head with a load of nonsense about how romantic it would be to run off with Philippe? It's just the sort of adolescent mumbo-jumbo a teenage girl would swallow, isn't it? The sort of thing one reads about in books—sweet innocent young girl swept off her feet by the handsome foreigner and defying everyone so that they can be together!' His voice was ice, cutting into her flesh, but Sarah seemed incapable of movement, of speech, of anything but standing there and listening to him, and that seemed to damn her even more in his eyes.

'So, nothing to say in your own defence? I knew I was right last night, and now I have the proof of it.' He let her go, contempt written all over his face. 'You filled my daughter's head with your own frustrated fantasies because you aren't capable of having an adult relationship with a man!'

The sound of her hand striking his face was loud in the silence which had fallen over the café, so loud that even she flinched. For a moment she stood and stared at him, watching the imprint of her hand turn from white to red, then she spun round on her heel and ran.

'Oh, no, you don't. You're not getting away with that!' He caught up with her at the bottom of the steps, his hands harsh as they caught her by the shoulders and hauled her round, but Sarah was beyond caring at that point. She thought she had sunk to rock-bottom all those years ago, thought that never again would she sink so low again, but she'd been wrong. His cruel, contemptuous words had opened up a wound that had been festering inside her for so long now, too long to even start to heal.

'The truth can be quite unpalatable when it's forced upon you, can't it, Sarah? But it's about time you faced up to what you are, and you're nothing but a frustrated spinster who gets her kicks from indoctrinating ideas into innocent heads!'

He shook her hard until her head seemed to swim with colours and she murmured incoherently, then suddenly found the strength to push him away. 'No. You're wrong, Mr MacAllister. Wrong...wrong...wrong!' Hysteria bubbled in her voice, found an outlet in a harshly bitter laugh which she tried her best to curb.

'I don't have romantic fantasies, Mr MacAllister, I have nightmares! Would you like to know why?' She was trembling now, she could feel it, feel the tension singing in her veins, feel the pain his cruel accusations had evoked. 'Would you really like to know why I'd never put such ideas into your daughter's head, why I haven't been making a play for you? I was...'

'*Excusez-moi, madame...monsieur.*'

The softly murmured apology from the man making his way from the café broke into her thoughts, splintering them like glass. For one horrified second, Sarah stared at James MacAllister, unable to believe what she had been about to say, then she turned and ran, ran and ran until she could run no further, but she couldn't run away from the nightmares of the past.

CHAPTER FOUR

THE sun slid behind a cloud, settling shadows across the broad sweep of the river.

Sarah plucked a stem of the rich grass and rolled it between her fingers, feeling its moist coolness against her hot, dry flesh. Now that the anger had faded so abruptly she felt drained, as though all the life had been sucked out of her, leaving her an empty shell. She'd tried so hard over the years to keep her emotions in check, yet in the past twenty-four hours all the barriers had been smashed, to leave her vulnerable once more. James MacAllister had destroyed them all.

'Are you all right?' His voice was soft, barely carrying above the soft sigh of the breeze in the trees, yet she still jumped. She shot a glance over her shoulder, feeling the blood swelling in her veins as she saw him standing behind her, his eyes shuttered. What was he thinking, feeling? Did he have any inkling of what she'd been about to tell him before? The thought made her feel sick, and she turned away to stare at the river, willing him to take the hint and leave, but it seemed that wasn't his intention.

He sat down beside her on the damp, springy grass, resting his forearms across his upbent knees as he too stared at the silvery swirl of water which flowed endlessly on its way.

'This reminds me of where I live,' he mused. 'I have a house down by the river and I never tire of watching the water. There's a special kind of peace about it, I find.'

Did he really expect her to make polite conversation after what had happened between them? It seemed he must, but before she could respond he carried on.

'I designed and built the house for my wife, Ruth...Catherine's mother. She loved the river and kept on asking me to find a suitable spot, but you know how it is—you keep on delaying doing a thing because other commitments seem more pressing.' He paused for a moment, the air charged with a kind of sadness that tugged at Sarah's raw emotions. 'By the time the house was completed she only had a chance to enjoy living there for a few months before she died.

'It's one of the few things that I regret in my life, that I never did what she wanted sooner so that she would have had more time there, but that's how it goes sometimes. No amount of regrets will change it.' He turned to look directly at her then, his eyes level, although Sarah could sense a certain watchful tension in him she'd never noticed before. 'You can't change the past, Sarah. You have to face up to it and accept it...whatever it is.'

Her face flamed with colour and she looked away, feeling her stomach churning. How much had he guessed? It was hard to recall exactly what she'd said in the heat of the moment, but surely she hadn't said enough to betray the secret she'd kept hidden for so long? 'I have no idea what you're talking about, Mr MacAllister, so save your advice for someone who needs it more.'

'James.' His voice betrayed nothing, his eyes still calm and level as he continued to watch her. 'We've gone beyond the point of squabbling over names, don't you agree? I would prefer it if you called me James.'

'Why? Because you imagine that will make up for what you said to me before, all those totally unfounded accusations? Or because you feel sorry because you upset me?' Sarah glared back at him, her emotions too close to the surface to allow herself to see the offer as anything else. 'Well, thank you very much, *Mr* MacAllister, but I think I'll pass on accepting that dubious honour! I don't need your apologies or your pity!'

She started to scramble to her feet, terrified that she would disgrace herself by breaking down, but he caught her by the elbow and pulled her back so that she fell to her knees in front of him. He was so close now that she could see the tiny lines fanned from the corners of his eyes, see the darkness of beard starting to shadow his jaw again. Instinct based on what had happened in the past told her that she should feel afraid at being held so close, but that wasn't how she felt at all, and that shocked her into remaining still.

'I wasn't offering you either, Sarah. I'm not fool enough to think you'd want them. All I was attempting to do was smooth our association, but obviously that's something you can't handle.'

He shook his head so that a lock of hair fell across his forehead, and Sarah clenched her hands, wondering at the sudden crazy urge she felt to smooth it back and feel the dark silkiness against her fingertips, such a contrast to the toughness of the man. 'I don't know what happened in your past, Sarah, that left you this way, but it must have been something traumatic.'

She stiffened at once, her eyes lifting to his in alarm. 'I don't know what you mean. Nothing happened in my past... nothing!'

He smiled almost gently, but there was nothing gentle about the searching scrutiny he subjected her to before she dropped her eyes to where his hand still lay fastened around her arm. 'We both know that's a lie. Whatever happened to you has left you a mess emotionally. Oh, you give off that aura of cold efficiency, but let anyone scratch the surface too deeply and underneath you're nothing but a terrified child who's still running from some nightmare. No wonder you find it hard to relate to real life, Sarah. You've spent your time locked well away from it because you're afraid to face up to it. That's why you filled Catherine's mind with all those foolish fantasies!'

'No!' She wrenched her arm away and sprang to her feet, filled with anger and a strange, inexplicable hurt that he should still insist on believing that. 'You're wrong, completely and utterly wrong, but obviously I shall never be able to convince you of that, so why continue to try? It's time this whole ridiculous charade was called to a halt. Obviously we can never hope to work together in any degree of harmony, so I think it's time we parted company. I shall go back to the café and phone the hotel and arrange to have Mrs Lawrence meet you in Limoges. It shouldn't cause too much of a delay.'

He came to his feet in one smooth lithe movement to stand towering over her, his face set into the uncompromising lines she was learning to recognise. 'There won't be any delay. Arrangements have already been made that you will accompany me, and that's the way they'll stand. I have no intention of making changes to my plans now.'

'Now look here, Mr MacAllister...' She flinched, every nerve contracting so that the blood stopped in her veins as he pressed a finger to her lips to halt the heated words.

'Save your breath. You're coming with me to find Catherine even if I have to tie you up and drag you with me. What happened before doesn't change a thing. My only interest is in finding my daughter, not in worrying about your hang-ups. She was your responsibility on this trip, and she will remain your responsibility until I have her safely back in my care. Now I suggest we get started. We've wasted far too much time today, thanks to you, as it is.'

He turned and walked back to the road, leaving Sarah staring after him with murder in her eyes. He really was the most insensitive, overbearing, arrogant man she had ever had the misfortune to meet! He didn't give a damn about anyone or anything. He just wanted to find Catherine so that he could get back to running his life without any more disruptions!

In furious silence she followed him back to the car, slamming the door behind her as she climbed in and sat stiffly in the seat. He started the engine, flicking her a hard glance as he eased out of the parking space.

'Instead of sitting there planning ways of getting even with me, Sarah, I suggest you try thinking back over anything that Catherine said which might give us a clue as to where she would stay. I'm no more anxious to spend time in your company than you obviously are to spend time in mine, so the faster we can find her, the faster we can go our separate ways.'

Sarah turned and smiled at him with a honeyed sweetness, venom dripping from her tones. 'What a marvellous thought. Believe me, Mr MacAllister, I shall rack my brains for any information she may have let slip if it will achieve that end!'

She'd expected him to be angry, so that it startled her when he laughed deeply as he swung the car back out on to the road. 'Well, well, Sarah, where did that come from?'

'What? I have no idea what you're talking about.'

'No?' He raised a thick black brow, his eyes filled with mockery as he shot a quick glance at her before turning his attention back to the road. 'As I recall, less than twenty-four hours ago it would have been unthinkable for the prim and proper Miss Marshall to snap back in that tone. You seem to be letting your hair down in more ways than one.'

The cool mockery brought colour to her face, and she turned away at once, hating him for what he'd said, especially when she was forced to admit that it was true. She would never have responded like that before, *never* have adopted that tone of voice with the parent of one of her pupils! She had always prided herself on maintaining a coolly professional approach in dealing with even the most infuriating parents. So what was it about James MacAllister that made her forget all those long-held principles and ideals? Was it just that he seemed to have the knack of rubbing her up the wrong way each time he spoke? Or was there another reason, a reason she wasn't prepared to delve too deeply into?

For all these long, lonely years she'd lived in an emotionless wasteland, terrified of ever letting her guard down, yet now she seemed incapable of maintaining those barriers any longer, and she was suddenly afraid.

The wind was rising, sending cold blasts of air into the room to chill her skin, but Sarah made no move to close the window. She stared out across the rooftops, watching the play of moonlight glinting off the wet tiles. It had started raining a few hours earlier, a heavy downpour which had swirled across the road, making driving conditions difficult, but it hadn't slowed James MacAllister down. Face set with a grim determination, he had carried on, seemingly tireless as he'd driven along the near-deserted roads. Sarah had started to wonder if he intended to drive all night, but she hadn't asked him, the same as she hadn't asked him to stop. She would ask no favours from him and give none in return. That seemed the safest way to handle this strangely turbulent relationship of theirs.

However, it had been a relief when he had finally turned off the main road and followed the signs to this small town where, as he'd curtly informed her, they would spend the night. Her head had been throbbing from the incessant noise of the engine and the tension, so that she had welcomed a break from both.

With a weary sigh, she closed the window and looked round the room, wondering if it was worth unpacking any of her clothes. It was almost nine o'clock already, and if she knew anything at all about James MacAllister it was that he wouldn't want to linger in the morning. He'd expect her to be up and ready at the crack of dawn and probably complain bitterly if she held him up for even a few minutes. It would be simpler to leave her things in the case rather than waste all that effort of unpacking them into the tall, old-fashioned armoire which smelled strongly of lavender, and get ready for bed.

She started to unbutton her blouse, then jumped nervously when there was a peremptory knock at the door. Hurriedly she refastened the buttons, colour staining her cheeks as memories of the previous night's interruption flooded into her mind. This time she had taken the precaution of locking her door as soon as she'd come into the room, but there was no way she could lock the unsettling memories from her head. They would stay with her for a long time to come!

It wasn't a surprise to find James MacAllister standing impatiently outside when she opened the door, but it was strangely disturbing. Just the sight of him seemed to make her emotions run wild, sending the blood thundering along her veins in a way that she found deeply unsettling. What was it about this man that disturbed her so? If she knew the answer to that then she would most probably know how to deal with him. It was the fact that she didn't that annoyed her so much, and it showed in the sharpness of her tone. 'Yes? Did you want me for something?'

One eyebrow quirked at the less than friendly greeting but he pointedly didn't comment. 'You'd better get a coat. It's still raining outside.'

'Coat? What on earth for?'

'Because we're going out for something to eat.' He moved past her into the room, filling the tiny space with its sloping eaves and heavy old-fashioned furniture with his bulk. Sarah pressed back against the wall to avoid touching him as he passed, feeling the heat run along her veins as he shot her a knowing look, his voice silky-smooth with mockery when he spoke again. 'Don't worry, I have no intention of repeating last night's mistake.' He ran his hand down his face, drawing her eyes to the scars on his lean cheek which had started to heal over. 'I was just looking for your coat so that we don't have to waste any more time than is necessary.'

It was difficult to remain calm in the face of such goading, but she managed it...just! 'I don't need a coat. Thank you for the offer, Mr MacAllister, but I'm not hungry. I don't wish to go out for a meal with you.'

'I'm afraid you seem to have misunderstood my meaning, Sarah. That wasn't an invitation, it was an order. Now get your coat and stop wasting more time arguing.'

'An order? Just who do you think you are? Do you really imagine that you can *order* me to eat, as though I were a child?' Fury rippled through her, gathering momentum with an alarming speed. 'Let me repeat what I said, Mr MacAllister. I have no intention of going out for any meal. Now, if that's perfectly clear, would you please leave?'

She held the door wide, anger glinting in her eyes, but he seemed unmoved as he stared calmly back at her.

'You've made yourself more than clear, Sarah, but I'm afraid your preferences are of little interest to me. All I'm concerned about is finding Catherine, and to do that I need to know if anyone has seen her.' He pulled the map out of his pocket and handed it to her, his eyes like flint.

'Take a good look at what's written in that margin. The writing is cramped, but it seemed to me that it mentions this place. Assuming that they set off and followed the route they'd worked out in advance then it's more than likely that this is where they intended to stop for the night. It's just possible that someone will remember seeing them, and the most likely place is in the local café. They must have had to eat somewhere, so I intend to ask around, and you, my dear Sarah, are coming with me. Frankly, you've been nothing but a hindrance so far, but you should make up for that with your knowledge of the language.' He glanced at his watch, his expression hardening. 'Now if it isn't too much to ask, will you get that coat so we can make a start? At this rate everyone will be in bed!'

Why did he always make her feel that she'd made a complete fool of herself? Sarah's face flamed as she collected her coat from the peg behind the door and dragged it on, walking past him without another word, although there was any amount of tart ones hovering on her tongue. That was the trouble, of course—instead of rationalising it out beforehand as she usually did, she tended to jump straight in when James MacAllister spoke, viewing his every word and action as some sort of personal attack. Naturally he would be anxious to start making enquiries straight away as to Catherine's whereabouts. There was always the slim chance that she might still be here.

Rain was gusting along the quiet street as they stepped from the shelter of the *auberge*'s doorway. Sarah pulled the collar of her coat up under her chin, jumping nervously when James MacAllister caught her arm and led her towards a side-road. 'From what I could gather from the woman who booked us in, the café is down here somewhere. Let's try it.'

Sarah nodded, trying unsuccessfully to inch her arm free of his grasp, but his hard fingers merely tightened, burning through the thin fabric of her cotton trenchcoat.

'Are you always this nervous about being touched?' He glanced down at her, his face shadowed as the moon slipped behind a heavy cloud. 'Or is it just with me that you react as though even the slightest touch is some sort of a violation?'

'Don't be ridiculous! Just because I don't appreciate being manhandled it doesn't mean I'm nervous!'

'Manhandled? I was merely being polite in offering you a helping hand. The ground's rather rough along here.' There was no mistaking the amusement in that deep voice, and Sarah snatched her arm away.

'Well, I don't need your help, thank you very much! I'm quite capable of walking unaided, Mr MacAllister, so save your gestures of "politeness" for someone who'll appreciate them!'

Was it fate that set the huge muddy puddle right in the middle of the lane and then made her miss seeing it as she marched ahead of him, her head tilted at a regal angle? She had no idea, but one moment she was marching along and the next she was up to her ankles in filthy icy water. Just for a moment she remained frozen to the spot, then she hurriedly scrambled out of the mud, glad of the darkness which hid her mortification from James MacAllister's eyes as he stood silently watching her.

Feeling in the pocket of her raincoat for a tissue, she bent and wiped at the filthy tidemark clinging to her ankles, wishing she were a million miles away. Why didn't he say something, anything, even 'I told you so', rather than stand there watching her that way?

She glanced up at him and felt her temper spill over as she saw that he was silently laughing at her futile attempts to clean herself up. Tossing the tissue aside, she swung round and started back the way they'd come, slithering to an inelegant halt when he unceremoniously hauled her back.

'And where do you think you're going?' The laughter had been replaced by a coldness that sent a shiver of ice sliding down her spine, and she stiffened at once.

'Back to the *auberge*, of course. I can't go anywhere in this state.'

He shook his head, the wind lifting the dark strands of hair from his forehead to blow it back so that his face looked stark and grim in the faint rays of moonlight. 'No way. We're not wasting any more time tonight. Come along.'

He pulled her with him as he started back along the lane, but Sarah resisted with a strength that surprised even her, her eyes spitting dislike at him. 'Just who do you think you are, bullying me like that? I'm going nowhere with you, James MacAllister, until I'm clean and dry!'

He stopped abruptly, catching her by the arms as he bent to stare straight into her face. 'I don't give a damn whether you're coated with mud from head to toe, lady, you aren't going anywhere until we've done what we set out to do! God knows I realised from the outset that you aren't the least concerned about Catherine, apart from the fact that her disappearance has disrupted your careful schedule, but I am! I need you to interpret for me, so you're coming with me whether you like it or not. Now we can do this the easy way or we can do it the hard way, but the outcome will be the same. You choose, Sarah, but make it quick, because I'm fast running out of patience.'

Why did she insist on arguing when she could see that he meant every word? Why didn't she just give in gracefully and get it over and done with? Normally that was exactly what she would have done, and yet...

'What do you mean, the easy way or the hard way? Are you threatening me? Let me tell you here and... Oh!'

Her scream cut through the night air, sharp with shock as he bent and flung her over his shoulder like a sack of coal before heading off down the lane. For a disbelieving moment Sarah remained rigid with shock, then she started to pummel his shoulders with her fists.

'Put me down! How dare you, you...you...?' Her vocabulary wasn't up to coping with such an event, and she dried up. Furious at her inability to express her feelings, she kicked her feet hard and felt a surge of satisfaction when she heard him curse roughly as her toe caught him a hard blow somewhere down his thigh. He stopped abruptly, letting her slide down to the ground, his face grim with fury.

'Do that again and I might be forced to forget that I'm a gentleman.'

'Huh! You wouldn't have the first idea of being a gentleman! A gentleman would never force a lady to go with him against her wishes!'

He smiled coldly, his eyes so dark that they gleamed with a black fire as they met hers. 'Probably not, but then I would hardly classify you as a lady, Sarah.' He caught her hand, rubbing her fingers down his cheek over the rough skin where the scratches had started to heal over. 'No *lady* would have done this, so I think this makes us even.'

Sarah drew in a shaky breath, feeling the anger fading. All she'd done was touch him, her fingers barely brushing over the lean, hard planes of his face, so why should that make her feel so... so strange?

She closed her eyes, terrified that he would read something from her expression, her voice strained when she spoke quietly. 'Let me go, James... please.'

She wasn't conscious of using his first name as she fought to control the feeling that her limbs were turning to water. It was only when he spoke that she realised what she'd done.

'Maybe we have made some progress after all. I don't make a habit of treating women in this chauvinistic fashion, Sarah, but it seems to have done the trick in breaking through that stiff reserve of yours.' He smiled faintly, his eyes shuttered as he looked down into her questioning face. 'You actually called me James, so maybe I've managed to make a dent in that iron-clad primness of yours.'

He moved back a couple of steps, but Sarah had the feeling that he would soon fetch her back if she made another attempt to turn back. That was why she stayed right where she was, she told herself, stayed still rather than face the indignity of a scuffle. It had nothing to do with this strangely debilitating weakness that seemed to have taken over her body.

She feigned a dismissive shrug. 'Mr MacAllister... James... what does it matter? Now shall we get on, if you're still intent on visiting that café? It's getting late.'

He stepped aside, gesturing mockingly for her to precede him. 'After you. I'm so glad we seem to be seeing eye to eye at last, Sarah. It should make things simpler if we don't waste time arguing.'

She doubted that very much! There was no way their relationship was ever going to be simple, from what she could see. Already it seemed to be incredibly complex, full of strange emotions bubbling just under the surface. Frankly, it was unlike anything she'd experienced before.

In silence they walked along the lane until they arrived at the café. With its peeling paintwork visible even in the dim light, it looked uninviting, but as James pushed the door open Sarah was surprised to find that it was full. She hesitated for a moment, uncomfortably aware of the way the conversation stopped as they appeared, but then James's fingers fastened around her elbow, hard and strangely reassuring. She glanced up at him, watching the way his eyes narrowed assessingly as he looked round the smoky room. He looked big and tough and uncompromising as he stood there, and suddenly she felt safer than she'd felt in ages. Whatever their differences, James would protect her, and the realisation made the first small dent in the wall of fear she'd surrounded herself with these past years.

'Let's sit over there.' He nodded towards a small table set in the corner of the room, retaining the comforting grip on her arm as he led her across to it. Settling himself in the straight-backed chair opposite hers, he glanced round, meeting the curious eyes of several of the men who were watching them, and somehow Sarah wasn't surprised to see that they looked away first. There was something intimidating about the way that James sat there so calmly exuding that aura of power and confidence. There would be few men who would choose to oppose him, she was sure.

'*Monsieur*?' The bar owner's tone was more curt than friendly as he came over to the table to take their order. James didn't acknowledge it as he ordered two cognacs without even bothering to ask Sarah what she wanted. He waited until the man had moved away, then glanced over at her, his eyes narrowing as he saw the faintly mutinous curve of her mouth.

'I know. Don't say it—you don't like cognac.' He felt in his pocket and pulled out a packet of cigarettes, lighting one before continuing. 'And no doubt you hate the smell of cigarettes.'

She shrugged, hating the fact that he could seemingly read her so easily. 'It's up to you if you want to ruin your health by smoking. As for the cognac—well, I happen to enjoy a glass now and again.'

He raised one dark brow, taking a draw on the cigarette before tilting his head to blow the smoke towards the ceiling. 'You do surprise me. I wouldn't have thought any kind of alcohol would be allowed past your lips. Whatever would your revered headmistress think of the very proper Miss Marshall enjoying a taste for cognac?'

Colour ran up her cheeks at his open goading, and she looked away. Why did he keep on doing it? What pleasure did it give him to remind her time after time of her status? 'I'm a free agent. It's up to me what I do once school hours are finished, Mr...' She stopped when he smiled cynically, the blush deepening. 'James,' she amended defiantly.

'Is it indeed? That comes as quite a shock, I must admit. I had the impression that school hours were *never* over, that your whole life revolved around your job to the exclusion of everything else. It would be interesting to delve deeper, Sarah—however, that really isn't why we're here. When the drinks come I want you to ask the man if he remembers seeing Catherine in here and how long ago it was.' He felt in his pocket again and pulled out a photograph, staring down at it with an expression of pain on his face before handing it across the table.

Sarah took the small photo, studying it as he had just done, marvelling that she had never really noticed before how like her father Catherine was. It was something about the set of the chin, the curve of the mouth. Unbidden, her eyes lifted to James's mouth as she examined the chiselled perfection of his masculine lips which held none of the softness of Catherine's. His lips would be hard and firm to touch. When he kissed a woman his mouth would burn its brand on to her, leave a mark that no other man's lips could erase.

The thought shocked her so much that unwillingly her eyes flew to his, wide, startled, betraying her shock at imagining such things. She had never thought about a man's mouth before, never imagined what it would feel like pressed against hers. It shocked her to the core that she should do so now about James MacAllister of all people!

'What's the matter?' He reached across the table and touched her hand, his long fingers cool against her heated flesh, drawing her abruptly back from that moment of madness. Sarah shivered, pulling her hand away to let it fall to her lap, but even then she could still feel the tingling imprint of his flesh on hers. 'Nothing.'

'Are you sure?' His voice was filled with a curiosity that terrified her. How he would mock her if he ever found out what she'd been thinking, ever found out that for one crazy moment she had wanted to feel his mouth on hers with a desire that defied all logic! 'Nothing's the matter. I told you——' She broke off in relief when the barman came back with the drinks, glad of the chance to change the subject. When the man turned to leave she stopped him, showing him the photograph while she asked him if he had ever seen the girl.

He barely glanced at it, tossing it down on to the table with a shake of his head before turning to go, but something made Sarah persist. She repeated the question, her voice sharp with authority, then felt her stomach lurch when he replied shortly before hurriedly walking away.

'Well, do I take it from that he hasn't seen her?' James picked up the photograph, balancing it in his hand as he stared grimly at Sarah across the table, and she drew in a shuddery little breath as she quickly ran back over what the man had said, trying desperately to see if she'd made some sort of mistake, but in her heart she knew she hadn't. 'Well, say something, why don't you?' There was impatience in James's voice as he waited for her to reply to his question, and hurriedly she tried to frame an answer.

'He said...' She stopped, swallowing hard against the knot of fear that was suddenly lodged in her throat. 'He said he hadn't seen them.'

Disappointment shone briefly in his eyes before they became shuttered once more. 'I see. Well, it was worth a try.' He picked up his glass and took a long swallow, then set it back down when she caught his arm, her fingers tightening around the hardness of the muscle.

'No! You don't understand, James. He...he said he hadn't seen *them*, but I didn't ask him that. I asked if he remembered seeing Catherine. I made no mention of her being with anyone else!'

His hand tightened into a fist, almost shattering the glass from the pressure before slowly and deliberately he set it away from him and stared back at her across the table with eyes like steel. 'Are you sure, Sarah? Absolutely certain? It's easy to make a mistake. Maybe you misunderstood what he said.'

'No.' She laughed a trifle bitterly. 'I know you don't have a very high opinion of me, but one thing I am good at is what I do for a living. I teach French, James, and I speak it extremely well. I made no mistake. It was quite clear what he said just now. The question is what are we going to do about it?'

'Do? Find out what's going on here, that's what we're going to do.' He picked up the glass and drained the last of the drink, his face set when he put it down and stood up. Sarah pushed back her chair, feeling a shiver of fear coursing through her when she saw the expression on his face as he dropped some money on to the table and picked up the photograph to slip it back into his pocket.

She followed him out of the café, almost running to keep up with him as he started back up the lane. 'James! For heaven's sake, wait!' She caught his sleeve, forcing him to slow down. 'Tell me what you're planning on doing.'

He swung round to look at her, dark and forbidding as he faced her. There was no mockery in his eyes now, none of that infuriating laughter which she'd grown almost accustomed to seeing. All there was in those flat black eyes was an anger that seemed to be directed straight at her.

'I'm going to take you back to the *auberge* and then I'm going to find out what's happened here.'

'Let me stay with you. Be sensible, James. You need me to help you ask questions.'

He shook his head, his expression filled with an icy contempt that cut straight into her heart. 'I don't want your help any longer. I can manage to make myself understood, I'm sure.'

'But what am I going to do?'

He laughed, no amusement in the sound, just an echo of something that made the hairs on the back of her neck lift. 'Pray, Sarah, just pray.' He moved suddenly, catching her chin to tilt her face so that he could stare into her eyes, and she caught her breath at the anger in his. 'Pray that nothing has happened to my daughter thanks to you!'

He let her go so abruptly that she staggered, turning away to walk back down the lane. She followed him in silence, feeling tears stinging at the back of her lids. He hated her, and nothing she said or did would ever make him change his mind. He still believed that she was responsible for Catherine's disappearance, and now all she could do was as he'd said—pray that it would all turn out right. If she added another silent prayer that one day he would accept the truth and forgive her, then who was to know apart from her?

CHAPTER FIVE

SARAH couldn't rest. It had been over an hour since James had left her at the door to the inn before returning to the café, and Sarah had spent that time pacing the floor of her room, worrying about what was happening. If only he had let her go back with him once they had made some plans—but he hadn't wanted that, of course. He'd made his feeling very plain about not needing her, and it still hurt to remember what he'd said in that icily cutting tone. Why should it suddenly matter so much what he thought about her? She didn't want to dwell on the reasons for it.

Pressing her face against the cool, damp glass, she peered out across the quiet street as she'd done a hundred times already, then gave a tiny murmur of relief when a tall, familiar figure suddenly appeared. She turned and ran to the door, hurrying along the narrow landing to wait at the top of the steep flight of stairs, a faint puzzlement on her face as she watched him slowly climb towards her. He seemed to be moving strangely, a stiffness to his body which was quite alien to his usual litheness. But it was only when he reached the top and stopped under the lamp that she saw the reason for it.

'James! What's happened? How did you get that cut on your forehead?' Instinctively she moved closer, her hand lifting towards the livid bruise on his left temple, but he pushed her aside, walking past her without a word.

Sarah watched him go with pain in her eyes that suddenly turned to determination. He mightn't want her to know what had gone on, might indeed refuse to tell her, but that didn't mean she wasn't going to try to find out. She'd be damned if she'd let him walk past her like that without saying a word!

She hurried after him, catching the door just as he started to close it, and followed him into his room. He tossed his coat on to the bed, then turned to look at her, his face set and unfriendly. 'I don't remember inviting you in. If you have something to say then get it over with. I'm not in the mood for any hysterical outbursts right now.'

'You won't get any. I just want to know what happened.' She swept a hand towards his face, her eyes lingering on the cut which was trickling blood down his cheek. 'And don't try telling me you walked into a wall, James MacAllister! It's obvious that you've been in a fight.'

His lip curled in derision as he started to unbutton his shirt. 'You seem very knowledgeable all of a sudden, *Miss* Marshall. How many fight victims have you seen, to make you such an expert?'

'I don't need to be an expert to recognise the mark of a fist! Is that what you did, went back to the café and started a fight? How could you be so stupid? What did you hope to achieve?'

He stripped the torn shirt down his arms and tossed it aside, his face set. 'I didn't start anything, for your information. All I did was ask a few more questions and showed the photo around to a couple of men. However, one or two of them seemed to take exception to my asking any questions. They started the fight... I merely finished it!'

'And what am I supposed to say to that? Well done? I'm afraid you've come to the wrong person if you want your male ego stroked, James MacAllister. It was a stupid, irresponsible thing to do, to go back there like that, and what did it achieve?' Sarah shook her head, fighting the images that were forming in her mind and making her feel sick, images of James being hurt. 'Nothing. A big fat painful nothing!'

He smiled tauntingly, moving slowly towards her. 'Who said it achieved nothing? I didn't. Now if you want to make yourself useful for once, see what you can do with this cut. I'm sure first aid is part of your teacher training, so let's see how good you are at your job, eh?'

He brushed past her, his bare chest brushing against her shoulder, sending a shaft of heat searing through the thin cotton of her blouse, making her suddenly vividly aware of his state of partial undress. She'd been so caught up in her anger before that she'd barely registered the fact that he had stripped off his shirt. Now her eyes were drawn to the hard, muscular perfection of his tanned torso with its covering of black hair arrowing down under his belt, and the room seemed to shrink. She couldn't stay in here with him like that, couldn't bear to be so close to him. She backed away, her eyes huge, frightened, and heard him sigh with a rough impatience.

'Don't bother—I'd hate to offend your delicate sensibilities again. Why don't you do us both a favour, Sarah, and leave? Then maybe I can do something with this and get some sleep.'

He ran water into the basin and picked up a wash-cloth, dabbing at the cut and wincing slightly. Sarah stood and watched him in silence while she fought a painful inner battle. One part of her mind told her to leave the room at once while the other part told her to stay and give him the help he needed. Which should she choose? How much longer could she allow the events of the past to direct her course of action?

She took a slow deep breath and walked over to him, silently taking the cloth from his hand to dip it into the cold water, willing him not to make some mocking, taunting comment, but he said nothing as he moved away to sit down on a chair set by the side of the narrow single bed. Sarah could feel him watching her, feel the heat running in trembling waves through her limbs, but she forced herself to carry on rinsing the cloth until the water was clean and fresh again. Wringing it out, she walked over to the chair and bent to press it gently but firmly against the cut on his temple, forcing her hands not to shake and betray her nervousness at being so close to him.

'How does it look?' His voice seemed to rumble in her ear, the deep tones sending a shiver like velvet smoothing over her skin coursing through her, and she flinched before she could stop herself. He swore softly, viciously, his hand closing over her slender wrist, his fingers encircling the delicate bones under the fine pale skin. 'Don't do that! I'm not going to hurt you—you must know that, so why keep on jumping all the time like some startled animal?' He moved her hand away from his face, tilting his head so that he could look her directly in the eyes. 'What is it with you, Sarah? Why are you so afraid of being close to me? Or is it just me? Maybe you're afraid of being close to any man.'

He was so near to the truth that she dragged her hand away, terrified that he would take that one small step needed towards understanding, and she couldn't have borne that, couldn't have stood to see the realisation in his eyes when he discovered her secret.

'Don't be ridiculous. I'm not afraid of you or anyone. You merely startled me, that's all. Now are you going to let me finish seeing to that cut or are we going to waste the rest of the night haggling over what you see as my hang-ups?' She smiled bitterly. 'That was the term you used previously, if I remember rightly, wasn't it?'

James sank back into the seat, staring calmly back at her. 'It was, and I was right. You have this deep aversion to being touched, and no matter how often you tell me that I *startled* you or whatever I won't believe you.'

'Well, that's your problem, I'm afraid. I can't help what you think.' She bent forward again, intent on cleaning the cut and getting out of the room as fast as she could, and overbalanced slightly in her haste. Instinctively she put her hand out to steady herself, her eyes flying to his as her fingers brushed softly against the smooth warmth of his bare skin. Under her finger-tips she could feel the hardness of muscle, the faint beating of his heart, and she froze.

His hand came up, covering hers, pressing her palm flat against his body as he held her there and stared back into her wide eyes. 'What does it feel like, Sarah, to touch another person like this, to let your skin meet mine? Does it frighten you, make you want to run away and hide again? Or does it make you want to explore further?' He lifted her hand slightly away from him, gliding her fingertips down from the smooth skin near his shoulder on to the hair-roughened skin of his chest, watching her face as he slid her hand slowly back and forth, burrowing her fingers into the thick mat of hair so that her nails grazed against his skin.

Her breath caught at the sensations that ran through her, sensations she'd never experienced before; sensations that drove all rational thought from her mind so that she could only stand helplessly in his grasp, watching her pale hand sliding back and forth across his darkly tanned chest.

'See, Sarah, there's nothing to be afraid of. I'm just flesh and blood like you.'

She shook her head, sending the long curls spilling from the knot at the back of her head to fall softly against her flushed cheeks. 'No, not like me...different.' Her voice was a low murmur, husky, betraying, and James smiled in obvious understanding.

'The same but different. That's the real joy, of course—the differences between a man and a woman.' His other hand came up to touch her face, lingering against the silkiness of her skin before he let it slide to the slender length of her throat, stroking gently up and down the delicate bones before coming to rest on the tiny pulse that was beating heavily at its base. 'It's just a pity that you never took the time to explore those differences before, isn't it, Sarah? Then maybe *we* wouldn't be here tonight, and maybe Catherine wouldn't be heaven knows where!'

The harsh accusation shattered the spell with devastating speed. Sarah stared at him in horror, then wrenched her hand away and stumbled backwards, feeling sick. It had all been a trick, a cruel, deliberate way to pay her back for what he believed she'd done in filling Catherine's head with romantic tales. What a fool she was, what a stupid, mindless fool, to have let him trick her that way!

Her face was ashen as she faced him, but she held herself rigid, refusing to give him the satisfaction of knowing how much he had hurt her. 'It seems you still wish to keep deluding yourself that this is my fault. Why? Because you can't face up to the truth and accept that if it's anyone's fault then it's yours? No matter. Frankly, I don't give a damn what you believe any longer. I just want to make one thing quite clear: if you ever touch me again then you'll regret it!'

He stood up, towering over her in the narrow space beside the bed. He was so close now that she could feel the heat from his bare torso seeping into her skin, sense the sheer physical power that those hard muscles had merely hinted at when she'd touched them. Just for a moment her mind committed the biggest treachery it could have done, allowing the sensations to come winging back before she ruthlessly suppressed them.

'And I want to make one thing clear too, Sarah, and that is that I shall never... *never*!... change my mind as to where the guilt lies.' He walked over to the door, holding it open, his eyes burning into her with anger in their depths. 'If anything has happened to my daughter then you'll regret being born!'

Sarah walked over to the door, her heart aching at the futility of it all. 'I hope nothing has happened to Catherine, not for my sake, or for yours, but because she's a lovely girl. Frankly, James, from the way you've behaved towards her these past months you don't deserve to have a daughter like her!'

He caught her arm as she started past him, his fingers biting cruelly into her flesh so that she knew she would have bruises on her arm in the morning. 'Don't push your luck, lady! I've had enough for one night, and it would take very little to tip me over the edge.'

'Over the edge into what? More violence? That doesn't appear to have achieved very much so far.' It was sheer bravado that kept her there, that plus a very real desire not to let him think he had won.

He smiled suddenly, his hand falling away from her arm. 'Who said anything about violence? I can think of a much more effective way of bringing you back in line, Sarah.' His eyes slid over her, blatantly insulting as they lingered on the slight curves of her slender body for a long moment before coming back to rest on her face. 'As for violence achieving nothing, that's where you're wrong.' He touched a finger to the bruise on his temple. 'This is a small price to pay for what I did manage to find out.'

'What are you talking about? Did someone say they'd seen Catherine in the café?' Sarah dragged her mind away from the threat implicit in his cold eyes, clinging hold of what he'd just said to steady herself. He was just trying to frighten her, that was all. He didn't mean he would actually... Her mind shied away from that, unable to cope with the thought.

'They did. I didn't get any details, partly because we hit a language barrier and were then rather rudely interrupted, but one man did say that he remembered seeing Catherine. What I want to know now is where and when, not to mention the reason why the owner of the café and several of his cronies seem so reluctant to talk about it.' He stared grimly past her, his face betraying little of the agony he must be going through. Sarah wished desperately that she could say something to comfort him despite their differences, but what? Until Catherine was found there would be little James would wish to hear from her that would ease his mind.

He seemed to collect himself all of a sudden, his face hard as he looked back at her. 'That's where you come in. We're going back to that café in the morning, and we aren't leaving there until I have a few answers. Now I suggest you get to bed and sleep. You'll need all your strength tomorrow, if I'm not mistaken. Someone here knows something, and I have every intention of finding out what even if I have to rip this whole town apart to do it.'

He closed the door, and Sarah turned slowly to head back to her room and get ready for bed, but sleep proved impossible. Quite apart from the very real worry about what had happened to Catherine, there was the small matter of what had happened just now between her and James. Every time she closed her eyes images started to paint themselves inside her head, vivid, disturbing images of her hand stroking over his chest, her fingers burrowing into that thick black hair.

She groaned softly, rolling over to press her hot face into the starched coolness of the pillow. She wanted her life back the way it had been before all this had happened. She didn't want these shocking, disturbing thoughts of James MacAllister to keep on tormenting her mind. Years ago she'd realised how she must live her life, and she didn't want to change that now, especially because of some infuriating man who alternately made her furiously angry... and drove her crazy!

The smell of rich coffee filled the small dining-room. Sarah nodded at the woman who ran the inn, then went and sat down at one of the small dark wood tables set by the window. There were few people in the rather cramped, panelled room, just a couple sitting at the next table and an elderly man who was just finishing his breakfast and preparing to leave. Sarah nodded at them, then quietly asked for coffee and a croissant, staring out of the window at the garden while she waited for it to be brought.

The sound of heavy masculine footsteps coming across the bare polished boards alerted her, and she took a deep breath, trying to stem the sudden instant upsurge her heart gave when she turned and saw James crossing the room towards her. Dressed in dark grey trousers and a paler grey shirt with the sleeves rolled up to his elbows, he looked fresh and vital, the bruise on his temple only adding to the aura of toughness. Having spent several disgusted minutes studying her own pale, wan appearance in the mirror before she'd come down, Sarah felt a quite understandable flicker of annoyance run through her. Obviously James MacAllister hadn't spent the night sleeplessly as she had done!

It was that more than anything, she told herself, that added a snap to her voice when she returned his greeting. It had nothing whatsoever to do with the way her pulse did a strange little wobble as he sat down at the table, his long legs brushing against hers in the cramped space available. She might have spent the night wrestling with all those vivid memories, but now it was morning and she fully intended to put them from her mind.

He studied her in silence for a brief moment, his dark eyes tracing over the shadows under her eyes, the pallor of her skin. 'You look like hell. I thought I told you to get some sleep. What were you doing all night long?'

Sarah flushed deeply, glaring back at him across the small table. 'Thank you, and good morning to you too! I don't remember asking for your opinion on my appearance, Mr MacAllister, so I'd be grateful if you'd keep it to yourself.'

'Mmm, touchy this morning, aren't we? And what's with the *Mr* MacAllister bit? I seem to remember that we moved our relationship along more than a step or two last night, Sarah.'

The dining-room was quiet, so quiet that his deep voice carried easily across the room to where the other couple were sitting. Sarah sensed rather than saw the speculation in the look they cast her way, and her face went beet-red. 'Do you mind?' she muttered, bending forward so that only he could hear. 'What are people going to think?'

He met her eyes calmly, one brow quirking upwards. 'I have no idea what you're talking about, Sarah.'

'Don't lie. You know very well that it sounded as though...as though...' How had she managed that, managed to back herself into such an uncomfortable corner quite so well?

He laughed softly, deeply, a low sound which stroked along her raw nerves, making her tingle in unwilling response. Reaching out, he captured her hand, his eyes mocking as he raised her fingers to his lips and brushed them lightly in a travesty of a kiss. 'As though we spent the night making love? Is that what you're so shy of saying? This is France, Sarah. The French understand such things so much better than we English do, so don't feel embarrassed, my sweet.'

'I...I...' The touch of those hard, cool lips had lit a fire inside her, a fire that seemed to burn with a heat that consumed her, melting away any vestiges of common sense for a crazy moment. Sarah drew in a deep breath, turning her head away from the dark intensity of that mocking gaze. Her eyes met those of the woman at the next table, who smiled at her with conspiratorial understanding, obviously enjoying what appeared to be such a tender exchange between lovers, and sanity returned with a vengeance. She snatched her hand away from him, murder in her eyes as she glared across the table. 'One of these days, James MacAllister, I'm going to make you pay for all this!'

'In other circumstances that could prove to be an interesting topic for discussion but right now I'm more concerned with the reason why we're here—namely Catherine.'

The shutters came down all at once, cutting off the mockery that had infuriated her so just a moment before. Sarah sat back, stunned by the sudden switch in his attitude. Why did he keep on doing that, changing the tone of their conversation so abruptly that she was left reeling?

Puzzling on his strange behaviour, she sipped the strong black coffee and ate the warm, buttery croissant, barely tasting either. James drank his coffee, then set the thick earthenware cup back on its saucer and stood up. 'Ready? We can't afford to waste any more time.'

There was a noticeable tension in the set of his hard, lean body that sent a warning shiver racing down her spine. Sarah slowly put the rest of the croissant back on the plate and wiped her fingers on the coarse cotton napkin. 'We won't achieve anything if you set off with that sort of attitude,' she said quietly. 'All you'll do is cause more trouble.'

'I never started the trouble last night...they did!' There was an uncompromising hardness in his voice as he stood impatiently by the table, and she sighed as she pushed her chair back.

'There could be a reasonable explanation for what happened.'

'Oh, yes? What? Why should anyone in this town be reluctant to answer a few simple questions if he has nothing to hide?' He moved aside for her to precede him from the dining-room, his hand hard and impersonal at the small of her back as he guided her through the narrow gaps between the tables.

'It probably isn't anything to do with people having something to hide.' Sarah stopped just outside the door, turning to look back at him. In the dim light coming through the small window set at the bottom of the stairs, his face looked stern and remote, his black eyes unreadable. She knew so little about James MacAllister, that was the trouble; she didn't know how to handle him, how to convince him that he had to approach this cautiously if they were to learn anything at all about Catherine's whereabouts.

'Then why did that barman tell us a lie? And why did his cronies try to dissuade me from making any further enquiries?' His lips curled into a cold smile. 'What's that saying about the innocent have nothing to hide? You can talk all you like and tell me to play things quietly, but don't forget that this is my daughter we're talking about, Sarah Marshall. If I have to take on every single man in this place to come up with some answers then I shall do it without a second thought!'

'We'll get nowhere if you start talking like that! Look, James, this is a small town, rather off the beaten track. It's not surprising that people here are very suspicious about answering questions. Surely you've met this attitude before in other places?'

'Of course I have. You don't need to lecture me about people's attitudes, Sarah. I'm not one of your pupils. I've been working in some small villages in South America that would make this place look like a city in comparison! I can well appreciate a natural reluctance to answer a stranger's questions, but last night was different.' He stared past her, his face set with remnants of the anger she'd witnessed when he'd come back to the inn the previous night mixed with a very real fear. 'They *know* something about Catherine and where she is, and it frightens me to imagine what that could mean.' He looked back at her suddenly, his eyes cold. 'Now, if you've quite finished with telling me what to do and how to act, I suggest we get along to that café. The sooner we can find what's been going on the better. As for *my* attitude, Sarah, then I shall leave all the talking in your supposedly capable hands and let you see what you can come up with. It's about time you made some amends for what you've done.'

He walked away, leaving her staring after him, not knowing whether to tell him to go to hell, or what! Just for a moment then she'd almost weakened when she'd seen the worry on his face, but that would have been a mistake. Give one inch to James MacAllister and she would soon find herself giving a mile as well. He was tough and hard and well able to look after himself, far more able than she seemed to be at doing the same. From here on she would do as he asked, no more and no less, and try to keep their relationship on a completely even keel. It worked better that way than when she allowed any emotions to make their way to the surface, as she knew to her cost. Last night should prove to be a salutary lesson if she was ever tempted to forget!

CHAPTER SIX

THE café was empty. Sarah walked across the room and sat down at the same table they had sat at the night before, hearing her footsteps echoing hollowly on the wooden floor. James pulled out a chair and sat down opposite her, drumming his fingers impatiently on the table as he glared round the empty room. It looked little better in the daylight than it had the previous night, the peeling paintwork and smoke stains on the cream-washed walls very much in evidence, and Sarah felt a flurry of anxiety ripple through her as she wondered what Catherine had been doing in such a place.

'Where the hell is everyone?' There was a rough impatience in James's voice which boded ill for their chances of asking questions in a civilised manner, and Sarah glared at him.

'Someone will be here in a moment. This isn't London, or even Paris. People don't come running at the first sign of a customer. The whole style of life is far more relaxed.'

He raised a mocking brow, a habit that Sarah was starting to recognise rather well. 'Another lesson, Miss Marshall, or just a wish to convince me that you know something about the country other than what you've read in books?'

'Sarcasm is rarely attractive, *Mr* MacAllister. As for my knowledge of the country and the people coming from books—well…' she shrugged carelessly '…it might surprise you to learn that, apart from spending a year studying here when I was at university, I also spent some time travelling throughout France during my vacations when I was a student. At the risk of sounding rather pompous, I think I can safely claim to know quite a lot about this country and its inhabitants.'

'It does surprise me. Oh, not that you know so much, but that you were ever that adventurous! It's hard to imagine you ever being a young and carefree student backpacking around a foreign country. What made you change your outlook so drastically, Sarah? Was it just the system that caught up with you, or was there some other deciding factor that influenced you so that you fell into the rather rigid lifestyle you seem to have adopted?'

'I have no idea what you're talking about!' Colour seeped under her skin, tinting it with a soft rose that made her look suddenly far younger than her true age, and James's eyes narrowed speculatively.

'I'm talking about the fact that your whole life revolves around that school and its routines.'

'You know nothing at all about my lifestyle.' She gave a high little laugh, false and breathless as it fell into the heavy silence that suddenly surrounded them.

'I know a lot more than you imagine. Catherine's letters recently have been filled with little else but your doings, or should I say lack of them?' He sat back in the chair, tilting it backwards so that it creaked alarmingly at the strain he was putting on the back legs. Despite the fact that there wasn't a single ounce of spare flesh on his lean frame, he was a big man, his body heavily muscled, as she knew from last night when she had touched him so intimately. Memories came spinning back, merging the previous night with the present moment, so that for a second she had difficulty in separating them. She could still feel how his skin had been under her fingers, still feel the abrasive rub of his body hair against her palm, and her mouth went dry.

She closed her eyes, blinking away the pictures that were forming in her mind, pictures she couldn't cope with now in the clear, revealing light of day when he was sitting there watching her with those too-seeing eyes. 'I don't intend to sit here discussing my personal life with you,' she said hoarsely.

'What is there to discuss? You teach at a school...end of story. The only life you have, it appears to me, is the fantasy one inside your head!'

The contempt in his hard voice cut into the pictures, turning them to dust, and she shook with a sudden bitter fury. 'Damn you to hell, James! You keep on, don't you? Keep on with your accusations—but why? What have I ever done to you?'

'Put my daughter in danger because of your silly, virginal fantasies, that's what!' The chair levelled as he leant forward across the table. 'Without your stupidity in putting those ideas into Catherine's head, none of this would have happened!'

'I tell you I didn't! I didn't put anything into her head! What will it take to convince you?'

'Nothing! Because there's no way you'll ever change my mind. No way that——' He broke off, tension showing in every rigid line as the owner of the café suddenly appeared. He went to push back his chair, but Sarah laid a restraining hand on his arm.

'No. Leave this to me.' She smiled bitterly. 'Perhaps this is one instance when I'm better qualified to deal with a situation than you are.'

She walked over to the counter, waiting patiently until the man was forced to look up, then spoke in perfect idiomatic French that he couldn't claim not to understand. The man answered in monosyllables at first, then finally broke into a torrent of agitated French when Sarah persisted.

'What's he saying? Does he admit that he's seen Catherine?' The undisguised anger in James's voice broke through the language barrier, and the man stopped abruptly, staring from one to the other with a hunted light in his eyes. Then suddenly he called over his shoulder, and Sarah felt her stomach lurch when a second, younger man appeared from the back room. From the bruises on his face and the way he glared at James, she realised he must be one of the men who had started the fight the previous night.

The two men conferred together, obviously arguing, although it was impossible to hear what they were saying. Then abruptly the owner seemed to come to a decision, ignoring the other man's protests as he turned back to them, and Sarah gasped in relief, only then willing to admit how worried she'd been.

'What did he say, Sarah? What?' James swung her round as the man stopped speaking, anxiety darkening his eyes, but Sarah pulled away from him and headed out of the door.

'If you don't tell me what was going on back there soon then I swear I won't be responsible for my actions!'

With a composure she was proud of, Sarah ignored him and walked a little way along the lane and sat down weakly on a stone wall. 'Are you always this belligerent?' she asked sweetly. 'Or should I consider myself honoured for having this sort of an effect on you?' She held her hand up when he made a threatening move towards her. 'All right, all right. Let's not resort to violence again. Perhaps if you'd managed to curb your temper a while longer last night then you would have found out that Catherine is quite safe.'

'She is?' The utter relief which crossed his face made her feel like a louse for delaying even for a moment telling him the good news. No matter what his faults were, and to her mind they were numerous, he did care about his daughter. Her voice softened unconsciously and she smiled at him with a genuine warmth.

'Yes. You were right; she was here yesterday with Philippe. That man was quite adamant about that.'

'Then why didn't he say so before? Why all the mystery?' He cast a harsh look back over his shoulder at the café. 'I fail to see what he stood to gain by keeping it all a secret.'

'It was a question of loyalty. You see, his son is a friend of Philippe's. That was him in the café just now, and I assume one of the men you met up with last night. He had persuaded his father not to mention anything about them being here.' She shrugged, tilting her face towards the warmth of the sun, feeling it ease the chill from her body. She had been so worried about Catherine after what James had found out, but at least now they knew she was safe, even if they didn't know exactly where she was.

'It doesn't add up,' he said. 'Why go to such lengths to stop me from finding anything out last night and then admit to it this morning?'

He moved closer, blocking the sun with his bulk as he stood towering over her. With the sun behind him, casting his face into shadow, it was hard to read his expression, but Sarah still sighed. She was coming to recognise that particular note in his voice rather well. He wouldn't be happy until she had told him the whole conversation virtually word for word. Was that the way he always conducted his affairs, digging out the facts and trusting nobody's judgement apart from his own? Probably. Despite the fact that he had been married and had a child there was a certain self-containment about James MacAllister that would be hard to breach. Would he unbend in a relationship with a woman? Would he allow her past those barriers he seemed to have surrounded himself with, let her touch the hidden core of himself? In his own way, he was as secretive as she was herself, and the realisation that she and James should have that in common shocked her.

'Well?' There was rough impatience in his tone as he prodded her for an answer, and reluctantly Sarah let the thoughts fade from her mind to be dealt with later, much, much later, in the privacy of her own room.

'I think it was the fact that I told him that you're Catherine's father, and that she's only fifteen years old. I don't think he liked the idea of having the local police around at the café asking questions about the disappearance of a minor, loyalty or no loyalty.'

'I see. I suppose it could make sense.' He ran a hand over his face, wincing slightly as he grazed the bruise on his temple, his eyes wry. 'I think I would have been better advised to leave it in your hands after all, Sarah. You seem to have achieved more than I managed to do.'

It was the first pleasant thing he'd ever really said to her, the first that didn't have a double-barbed edge, and she felt a rush of pleasure she couldn't hide. Abruptly she stood up, not wanting him to think that she was acting like some silly schoolgirl, hanging on to his every compliment, then staggered as her foot caught against one of the loose stones which littered the uneven ground.

'Careful!' His hand was strong against her waist as he steadied her, strong and warm and hard, as the rest of his body had felt last night. She knew nothing at all about men, had always been afraid of their strength before. So why was it that she felt her pulse quicken when James touched her like that? Why was it that she suddenly yearned for something she barely understood?

Something must have shown in her expression, because she heard him draw in a sudden breath and for a moment his fingers tightened against her waist before abruptly he let his hand drop to his side. 'You want to watch where you're walking. We don't want any accidents to slow us down.'

His tone was coolly impersonal, cutting her to the quick. She turned away, hiding the fleeting pain deep in her eyes, the sense of loss which shocked her. James MacAllister had never even pretended an interest in her as a person. She was here on sufferance to make amends for what she'd done, or what he believed she'd done. Why should it hurt her so that he should deliberately reject that fleeting moment of closeness?

Her voice was cool and stiff, controlling the hurt as she'd learned to do over the years. 'You can rest assured that I shall take more care in future. Now, what happens next?'

He moved away from her, remote and stern as he shot a fleeting look back at the café. 'We go on, of course. I take it that there was no mention made of Catherine's plans?' When she shook her head, he continued quickly, 'Right, then we can only assume that they intend to stick to the route they worked out. They stopped off here, obviously as planned, so it seems a safe assumption to make. That being so, I suggest we go back to the inn and pack.'

He turned and started back along the lane, his long legs eating up the ground, but for several minutes Sarah made no move to follow him.

At the end of this search, with any luck he would achieve his goal; he would have his daughter back, safe and well—but what about her? What would she have at the end? Would she be able to return to her former life and pick up the threads of her careful existence? Or would she discover that her life had altered so drastically that that wouldn't be enough?

She shaded her eyes against the glare as she watched the tall figure walking ahead of her and felt a sudden ache in her heart. What would life be like once James MacAllister was no longer a part of it? He infuriated her with his arrogance, his steely assertions that he was always right and she was wrong, frightened her by his very masculinity, but when this finally ended then she knew that her life would be lonelier and emptier than before.

* * *

The sun was setting, tinting the snowy peaks of the Pyrenees a delicate pink. They had come five hundred miles from Paris, but to Sarah's eyes they could have stepped on to a new planet. The whole area was so different, with its swift mountain streams, its lush valleys and medieval hilltop castles. She'd never visited this region before and would have loved to stop for a few moments to enjoy the view and savour the quiet which the few cars they had passed couldn't spoil, but James refused to waste any time. They had stopped just twice on the journey, once to ask around a small town that had been marked on the map and a second time to buy bread and cheese to eat, but that had been it. Now Sarah's whole body was aching with weariness, her muscles cramped from sitting in the seat for so long. Although she refused to ask him for favours, common sense dictated that they must stop soon before the sun slid down behind the towering peaks and left the countryside in darkness.

'How much further do you plan on going tonight?' she asked. 'It will be dark soon.'

He flicked her a cool glance, switching on his sidelights as the sun slid another inch or so out of sight. 'I don't intend to stop. We're not that far away from Philippe's home now. Another two or three hours and we should be there.'

'But how can you be sure of finding the village in the dark? From what I can tell by the map, it's way off the beaten track. It's foolish to go driving around in this sort of countryside in the dark!'

'I have no intention of allowing my daughter to spend another night in that fellow's company. Is that clear? I intend to drive all night long if that's what it takes, so resign yourself to the fact. This isn't a social outing, Sarah. We aren't here to enjoy ourselves, book in to a nice comfortable little inn and have a pleasant evening. We're here to find Catherine.'

'Pleasant evening...with you as company? Fat chance of that!'

He smiled faintly. 'You mean you didn't enjoy last night's little interlude? You surprise me, Sarah. I had the feeling that my...company wasn't completely abhorrent to you last night.'

She knew what he meant, of course, knew but didn't dare look at him in case he could see the awareness on her face. Turning her head, she stared out of the window, willing the foolish beating of her heart to slow, and heard him laugh, softly, deeply, an intimate sound that made the blood flurry along her veins.

'You really should learn to hide your feelings better, Sarah. How old are you? Thirty-eight...nine? Yet you don't seem to understand the first thing about the games men and women play. Can you really be so untouched and virginal, or is it all an act to hide your true colours?'

Anger rose at the over-estimation of her true age, to be replaced by a sudden swift, knifing pain as he continued. Untouched and virginal! If only he knew...if only he knew how much she wished that were true! With a force that staggered her the nightmare came flooding back all at once, and she gasped at the agony of it.

'What's the matter? Are you all right?' James took his eyes from the road to look at her, but she averted her gaze, not wanting him to see an echo of that pain.

'For heaven's sake, woman, answer me, can't you?' There was impatience in his hard voice that stung, and she shot him a quick look. It was all his fault, of course. He had come into her life and broken down the barriers, letting the hurt come flooding back, and now she rounded on him and gave vent to all the pent-up frustration she felt.

'Nothing! What is it with you, James? Why do you always think you have a right to know things that are no concern of yours? Why don't you just mind your own——?' She broke off, then shouted a warning, her voice rising in concern as a dark shadow seemed to hurl itself across the road in front of the car. 'Look out!'

James reacted instinctively to her cry, wrenching on the steering-wheel to send the car skidding to a halt at the side of the road, cursing fluently when there was an ominous crunch of metal. He cut the engine and climbed out without a word, walking back a little way as he searched the road for what had caused her to call out like that, but obviously found nothing. Sarah sank down in her seat as he came back and opened her door, then bent down to stare at her. 'Well?'

'I... I saw something running into the road—a deer, or a sheep or... something.' The way he was looking at her was making her nervous, and she sank another inch lower in the seat.

'A deer? Or a sheep? Or... something?' His voice was so calm, so gentle that for a moment she was lulled into a false sense of security and half smiled at him in relief.

'Yes, that's what it looked like. I didn't want you to hit it, so I called out to warn you.'

'I see. You really thought it worth risking both our lives just for a deer or a sheep? Are you completely stupid? Didn't common sense tell you not to shout out like that?'

'I... No! Look, I'm sorry, but how was I supposed to know you'd swerve across the road?'

'Most people would if some idiot had just screamed, "Look out!" in their ear! Now let's just hope that the car isn't too badly damaged, otherwise, lady, you're going to regret ever opening your mouth!'

James slammed the door, then bent down to peer under the car, working slowly and methodically as he checked each inch of the chassis, then stood up and brushed the dirt off his hands as he slid behind the wheel. Sarah held her breath, then let it out slowly as the engine caught immediately and settled into its familiar throb. So far so good.

James edged the car back on to the road, taking it gently at first before starting to pick up speed, but they'd gone not more than half a mile when he started to curse fluently. He pulled into the side of the road, his face like thunder as he studied the instruments on the dashboard.

'What is it? Is there something wrong?' Sarah's voice was hesitant, filled with more than a hint of apology as she turned slightly in her seat to see what was causing him so much concern, but it did little to mollify him.

He glared back at her, then pointed a finger at a light that was gleaming brightly on the panel. 'Can't you see?' he snapped, making no pretence of being polite.

'I... I'm afraid I don't drive,' she admitted in a low voice. 'I don't know a thing about cars.'

'Don't drive? I might have known it!' There was contempt in the statement, and she felt tears gather at the back of her eyes and quickly blinked them away.

'Well, I'm very sorry if that annoys you,' she said snappily to hide her distress, 'but frankly I've never had any reason to learn nor any desire to do so. Now, if it isn't too much to ask, maybe you can explain in terms I can understand what the trouble is.'

'Oh, I can explain all right, very simply. The car's had it. We won't be going anywhere in it tonight, thanks to you and your deer, or your sheep, or something!'

It was hard not to respond in kind, hard to keep a grip on her temper, which was starting to spiral up to meet his own, but Sarah managed it. 'Why? What's happened to it? Can't you fix it?'

'No, I can't.' James tapped the dashboard, then switched off the engine so that the glowing light faded abruptly. 'Obviously we hit something back there that's damaged the sump. That light was warning us that we're out of oil. There's no way we can go any further without the engine seizing up.'

'But what are we going to do?' Sarah stared at him in horror, then cast a despairing look out of the window. The shadows had lengthened now, staining the countryside with pools of darkness. In a short time it would be completely dark, leaving them stranded in the middle of nowhere.

'Seems to me we have two choices.' He stretched, easing the stiff muscles in his back before flexing his shoulders. Just for a second his arm brushed against hers, and she drew back at once, ignoring the hard stare he gave her.

'What choices?' Her voice seemed to echo in the stillness, faint, almost fragile. Now that they had stopped there was little noise to disturb the peace of the mountains, just the soft swish of a stream flowing down a nearby valley, the sigh of the wind blowing across the grass. The very stillness and solitude cast a feeling of intimacy over them as they sat close together in the car, an intimacy that made her feel nervous and restless at one and the same time. If the car wouldn't go then they would be forced to spend the night here, alone together, shut in its close confines.

'We can try walking to the nearest village or we can spend the night here and hope that someone will come along and offer help.'

Was it her imagination, or did his voice sound deeper, smoother, the rich tones flowing like wine through every overstretched nerve in her body? Sarah shook her head to dispel such crazy thoughts, but it was impossible to wipe an echo of the nervousness she felt from her voice. 'How far is it to the closest village?' she asked. 'It would be more sensible to try and walk there, surely, than spend the night in the car.'

'A good twenty kilometres at a rough guess.'

'Twenty kil... Why, that's miles away!'

'About twelve or so.'

'Then that's impossible. We can't go walking all that way in the dark!' Her options hadn't been numerous in the first place, and now they were whittling down to zero. How was she going to cope with the coming hours sharing the car with James in such closely intimate circumstances? Desperation made her open the car door and climb out as she stared back the way they had come, hoping to see the lights of another vehicle, but the road was empty, the sigh of the wind the only noise to be heard. Now that the sun had all but disappeared, the air was starting to turn chilly, carrying the sting of ice from the top of the mountains. Sarah shivered, hugging her arms around her body as she stared round, fighting the moment when she would be forced to get back inside the car and accept what fate and her own impetuosity had doled out to her—a night alone with James MacAllister in the middle of nowhere!

'You're going to catch cold. Get in.' It was more an order than a request, the brusqueness grating on her nerves like chalk on a board, and she flicked him a haughty glance. 'I'm fine. I'll get in when I want to, thank you.'

'Please yourself.' He climbed out of the car, pulling a sweatshirt from the back seat and dragging it over his head before walking off in the direction of a clump of stunted trees.

'Wait! Where are you going?' Sarah half started to follow him, then stopped when he shot a mocking look over his shoulder.

'It may have escaped your notice, but facilities hereabout are somewhat limited. We shall just have to make the best of things, I'm afraid.'

'Facilities? Oh . . . !' She was glad of the encroaching darkness as she suddenly caught his drift. Abruptly she turned back to the car and climbed inside, feeling her face burning with embarrassment. It was bad enough that they were seemingly stuck out here, but even worse when one considered that they wouldn't have even the comfort of basic toilet facilities! Why had she shouted out like that? Now her only hope lay in someone coming along who would be willing to help them.

The minutes ticked slowly away and the sun disappeared with a final flourish behind the peaks, leaving the whole countryside in darkness. Sarah peered at her watch, trying to work out how long it would be before morning came—then froze when she heard the sound of a car engine. Just for a moment shock held her immobile before she hurriedly came to her senses, realising with a flash of relief that help might be at hand sooner than anticipated. She scrambled from the car and ran into the road, waving her arms at the approaching vehicle to flag it down.

'Look out!' Arms fastened vice-like around her middle to swing her off her feet and out of the way as the car rushed past so close that she could actually feel the heat from its engine.

'Of all the stupid, idiotic things to do, that has to be the stupidest! What did you think you were doing hurling yourself into the road like that? Well, answer me then!' James shook her hard so that her head lolled like a rag doll's, his fingers bruising as they bit into her flesh. 'You could have been killed if I hadn't come back in time!'

Sarah shuddered, unwilling to admit what a close call it had been. She'd been so sure the car would stop, but... She pulled away from the rough grasp of James's hands. 'I was trying to get help, that was all. How was I to know that lunatic would almost mow me down?'

'Just by a bit of simple deduction!' He cast a disparaging look at the dark sky, then glowered back at her. 'It's pitch-black out here. I doubt if he had a chance to even see you before he was almost upon you! Don't you ever stop long enough to think before you rush into doing something?'

She laughed bitterly, more shaken than she cared to admit. 'Well, that makes a change. Now you're accusing me of acting rashly, yet this morning you were intent on telling me what a rigidly regimented person I am. The two don't seem to sit side by side, do they?'

'No? I think one is merely the result of the other. You've spent so many years living to a strict routine that once you deviate from it you go right off the tracks! Now, if you've quite finished causing trouble for one night, I suggest we get back in the car. From the feel of it, the temperature's dropping rapidly, and we don't want to end up suffering from exposure to add to all our other troubles.'

All the troubles she'd caused, he meant. Oh, he hadn't actually said that, but it had been evident from his tone that that was what he meant. He must have a very low opinion of her, and it didn't seem likely that it was going to change, not when she kept on doing all these silly things. What was the matter with her lately? For a sane and responsible adult who held down a highly respectable job she was making a real mess of everything!

In silence Sarah followed his lead and climbed into the car, edging over against the door so that she could leave a gap between them. As he had said, it was starting to get cold—very cold, the windscreen misting with the warmth of their breath. Surreptitiously she rubbed her hands up and down her arms to ward off the chill, but it achieved little apart from earning a quick look from James.

'Cold?' he asked.

She nodded, huddling deeper into the seat, avoiding his searching look until she heard him sigh noisily as he started to strip off the sweatshirt.

'Intent on playing the martyr, are you? Frankly, Sarah, you asked for everything I said back there, plus some. Here, put this on. It'll keep you warm.'

He handed her the sweater, but she shook her head, defiance in her soft grey-blue eyes. 'No, thank you. If I'm cold I have some clothes in my bag. I'll get something out of there.'

'What? Another of those prim little cardigans or neat little blouses? You need something more substantial than that.' He reached across the narrow space and caught her wrist to pull her towards him, his eyes narrowing as she immediately tried to pull away. 'Don't worry, sweetheart, I'm not about to ravish you. I simply intend to see that you don't end up with pneumonia and cause me yet more problems.'

With an economy of movement he pulled the sweatshirt over her head, sliding his hand inside to catch her arm and slip it through the sleeve when she made no attempt to help him. His knuckles brushed lightly against the swell of her breast, and she sucked in a deep breath as her nipple responded to the brief touch. Deep inside something jolted to life, a heavy, steady throb which seemed to fill her whole body with its force and rhythm, and she stiffened at once.

'I . . . I can do it.' Her fingers were all thumbs as she tried to ease the soft warm cloth from his grasp, but he refused to let it go. His hands stilled, hard and warm as they rested against her slender body under the folds of the sweatshirt. She could feel their warmth burning through her blouse, feel the strength of those long fingers resting so lightly yet so devastatingly against her waist, and her heart seemed to swell with emotions she'd never felt before.

Why should it feel so intimate to have James's hands resting quietly against her like this? If fiction was to be believed then intimacy could only be achieved by undressing, but James wasn't trying to do that.

When his hand moved slowly to catch her wrist under the folds of the sweater and ease it into the sleeve, she made no move to stop him, couldn't have stopped him if her life had depended on it. The touch of his hand seemed to have drawn all her strength away so that she sat quiescent, feeling his fingers glide down her arm again, lightly, gently, once the sleeve was fitted into place, to catch her other wrist and repeat the process. His fingers left a tingling sensation on her skin as he withdrew his hand, and she shivered in an unwitting response and felt his hand still for a moment that seemed to hold all eternity in its grasp.

'James...' His name was soft on her lips, so soft that it barely disturbed the deep silence that had fallen between them, yet she knew he'd heard, knew from the way his eyes met hers that he understood what she barely understood herself. Slowly, so slowly that it seemed like a dream, he bent and touched his mouth to hers, kissing her so gently that when he drew away she wondered if she'd imagined that soft, brief touch, but there was no way that imagination could have left behind the tingling sensation of warmth that melted away half a lifetime of frozen pain.

'James, I...'

'I'll just get another sweater out of my case.' With an abruptness that was shattering he turned away from her and opened the car door, slamming it forcibly behind him as he moved round to the boot. Sarah swallowed hard, feeling the heaviness of tears in her eyes. If he had come out and stated it he couldn't have made his feelings more plain, couldn't have told her that he regretted that impulsive act of kissing her. He shouldn't blame himself, though. The fault was hers. She might be totally inexperienced, but even she knew that when she'd said his name that way and looked at him it had been a blatant invitation!

She closed her eyes, huddling miserably in the seat as she heard him close the boot and come back to climb behind the wheel.

'We may as well try to get some sleep. If no one comes along in the morning we might have to make that walk to the village, so we'll need to save our strength.'

His voice was cool, impersonal, telling her so clearly that what had happened between them was over and done with as far as he was concerned. It had been a momentary lapse not to be repeated. They would forget all about it like two sensible people, but in her heart Sarah knew that she would never forget that brief moment when heaven had lain open to her.

If James had turned to her then and opened his arms, would she have gone into them without a thought for the past?

CHAPTER SEVEN

DEEP down Sarah knew it was a dream, knew that if she could only snap the clinging web of the nightmare she would be free, but it was impossible now that it was unfolding step by familiar, painful step.

She moved restlessly, her head twisting against the soft leather of the seat, her eyelids flickering as the pictures started to appear, pictures that had haunted her for years.

'No! No...please...no!' Her voice was hoarse, terrified, cutting through the quietness yet echoing inside her own head, and the very evidence of her fear seemed to make her even more afraid. When hands gripped her hard, she screamed, her voice lifting to a keening wail, before dropping to a sobbing, incoherent murmur which seemed to go on and on endlessly.

'Sarah! Wake up...come on, wake up!'

She was being lifted now, her body limp, bathed in perspiration, her heart spinning the blood through her veins so that her head was muzzy with the force of it, yet instinctively she struggled, twisting and turning, clawing at the hands that were holding her. There was a harsh exclamation, then something caught her cheek, stinging her awake and out of the clutches of the nightmare with an abruptness that left her disorientated. Shaking, she stared at the figure bending over her, her eyes dilated, huge, as she tried to get herself under control again. She touched her cheek, feeling the faint tenderness, the heat under the skin where James's hand had hit her, and swallowed hard.

'You were having a nightmare. I had to hit you—I'm sorry.' His voice was hard, curt, and she nodded as she turned away to stare blankly through the window at the darkness. What had she said? How much had she betrayed of the terror she always felt when the dream started, the utter helplessness? She couldn't bear for him to know!

A light flared, startling her so that she jumped and swung round to look at him, her eyes meeting his for a moment before skittering away again. In the dim glow cast by the interior light it was hard to read his expression, hard to tell what he was thinking behind that bland smooth mask.

'Want to talk about it?' His voice was low, betraying little. Sarah shook her head, feeling her hair falling around her face now that the pins had worked free.

'It could help. I have the feeling that wasn't the first time you've had that dream, was it?'

'No.' Her throat was dry, rasping as she tried to force the word out, even more painful when she realised how he might interpret her reply. 'I mean no, I don't want to talk about it. It was just a bad dream, that's all.'

'So bad that you were fighting like a madwoman? So bad that you were screaming as though your very life were in danger? Damn it, Sarah, don't lie! You've had that dream before, haven't you? Why? Was it something that happened to you? Were you reliving it again?'

Fear loosened her throat, sent the hurried denial of the truth rushing out. 'No! It was a dream, that's all.

Don't you ever have bad dreams yourself, or is the great James MacAllister impervious to that sort of thing?'

'Oh, I have nightmares. I've had more than a few these past days wondering what's happened to Catherine. But I don't recall ever feeling the kind of terror you were exhibiting just now, Sarah.'

'I...' She turned away, unable to cope with his probing scrutiny.

'Whatever it was, it still has the power to hurt you far more than it should. Why not tell me about it, Sarah? Maybe it would help to talk it through.' His voice held a note of compassion, and just for a moment she was tempted to pour it all out, to finally share the secret she had guarded so closely all these years; but then abruptly sanity returned. How could she tell him? How could she sit there and watch that compassion turn to disgust or contempt?

'There's nothing to tell. It was just a horrible dream, that's all.'

'Have it your way. I can't make you tell me. But nothing will change my mind, Sarah. There was more to that... *dream* than you're admitting.'

The hard assurance in his tone stung, and she rounded on him at once. 'Who do you think you are, to sit there and tell me what I'm dreaming about and why? You're incredible, James MacAllister! Totally unbelievable, with your arrogance, your absolute conviction that you're always right. No wonder Catherine has found it difficult to talk to you recently. I doubt if you ever truly listen to what she tells you!'

His face darkened with anger, all traces of compassion fading, to leave his face like a mask. 'I'm not interested in discussing my relationship with my daughter. We were talking about you, Sarah. Does that make you feel uncomfortable? Is that why you're trying to change the subject?'

'I... no!'

He ignored her protest, staring intently at her, obviously not prepared to give an inch. How she regretted her hasty words, regretted starting this fresh confrontation. She should have learned from experience that she always seemed to come off worst whenever they argued!

'It seems to me that the real trouble lies with your refusal to talk about this trauma in your life. Maybe if you had it wouldn't be haunting you now.'

He shrugged lightly, not taking his eyes from her face. 'You can lie all you like, make any kind of excuse, but that wasn't merely a "bad dream", was it? It was a nightmare you've had before, time and time again. A nightmare that stems from something that happened to you in the past.'

'No.' She wanted to shout the denial at him, shout it hard and clearly back in his arrogant face, but the word came out more as a whispered plea than anything else. Anger drained from her, leaving her shivering as she acknowledged how right he was. Was he right also to say that she should have talked about it before? Should she have told this horrible dark secret and maybe found a way to let the wounds heal?

Silence fell between them, a brooding silence that held a waiting expectancy that made her nerves raw with strain. Then suddenly she heard James sigh softly.

'Forget it, Sarah. It's too late, and I'm far too tired to carry on with this sort of discussion. We'd be better advised to try to get some sleep if we can.'

He switched off the interior light, plunging the car into darkness once more. Sarah huddled against the door, hearing the faint sounds of James settling back in his seat. She glanced over at him, straining her eyes so that she could just make out the outline of his clear-cut profile etched against the darkness of the window. From what she could tell he seemed to have closed his eyes and be trying to sleep, and how she envied him that ability! She wouldn't be able to sleep now, not after that argument they'd had and with the memory of the nightmare still so vividly fresh.

His head turned towards her all at once and she started nervously, feeling her heart leaping crazily inside her chest. Abruptly she turned away, resting her head against the cold hardness of the door panel, feeling more alone than she'd felt in the whole of her life. A single lonely tear slid down her cheek, and she brushed it away with a shaking hand, terrified that if she let her control slip she wouldn't be able to stop.

'For heaven's sake!' His voice was rough with impatience, yet his hands were gentle as he caught hold of her shoulders and turned her to face him, pulling her so close that Sarah could see the gleam of his eyes even through the darkness which enclosed them. Instinctively, she tried to break free, but he held her firmly, his arms around her slender body as he held her to him and nestled her head into the hollow of his shoulder. When he spoke his voice seemed to rumble through his body, sending tingling vibrations spreading along her taut nerves, vibrations that warmed and eased the pain of loneliness. 'Perhaps I was a bit rough on you just now. You're obviously still upset, but try to relax. It's unlikely that you'll have that nightmare again tonight, isn't it? Try to get some sleep now.'

His big warm hand smoothed her hair, stroking along the silky length before his fingers slid to the nape of her neck while he massaged the tense muscles. Sarah wanted to tell him to stop, but for some reason the words wouldn't come as each steady sweep of those long fingers sapped her resistance.

Slowly, reluctantly, she allowed her stiff body to relax against the warmth of his and felt his arms tighten as he settled her closer until she could feel the heavy thud of his heart against her breast. She caught her breath at the sensations that suddenly swamped her, sensations of intimacy at being held so close.

'All right?' His voice held a note that sent an unwilling responsive shiver through her, and she nodded, afraid to speak and betray how very vulnerable she felt. His hand stilled for an instant, then he resumed the steady rhythm, burrowing his fingertips through the thickness of her hair so that she could feel them gliding across her scalp. She closed her eyes, losing herself in the strangely seductive rhythm and the feeling of peace and security. It had been a long time since she'd felt like this—warm, secure, cared for. Too long, in fact.

When his hand stilled, she nuzzled her head against him like a kitten, wanting the soothing stroking to continue, and heard him laugh softly.

'Like this, do you?' His voice was soft, his breath stirring the curls at her temple, warm and moist as it flowed against her skin, and she shivered delicately, turning her face into the hard strength of his shoulder and wishing in her heart that this moment could go on forever; but of course it couldn't. She was Sarah Marshall, schoolteacher, he was James MacAllister, father of one of her pupils, and that was all there could ever be between them.

A deep sadness welled inside her and just for a moment her hand lifted as though to touch him before she let it fall silently back to her side. He was offering comfort to her, no more and no less than he would do for any woman he found himself stranded with in similar circumstances. She would be foolish beyond belief to see anything more than that in this precious little interlude of peace.

'Are you all right?' He asked the question quietly, his fingers sliding round to catch her chin and tilt her face up to his, and Sarah was glad of the darkness which hid her feelings from him.

'Yes.' Her voice was equally quiet, the one brief word the only one she could manage, the only one she imagined would be safe, but somehow James must have sensed the sadness from her tone. His hand slid up to her cheek, cupping it as he tilted her face a fraction more and bent to peer more closely into her eyes.

'Are you sure?'

Even that single word was beyond her now as she felt the searching scrutiny, and she nodded mutely, feeling his fingers sliding against the cool smoothness of her cheek as she moved her head. Sensation flowed between them, arcing through the darkness in a sudden fierce surge that caught her breath and made her heart start to hammer so loudly that she knew he must hear. There was a moment, just one, when the whole world ground to a halt, then James muttered harshly under his breath and bent towards her just as she lifted her head to move away from the burning touch of his hand.

Their lips brushed, touched, clung, then slowly parted in a silence that seemed to be so deep, it enclosed them from the rest of the world.

'Sarah, I... Oh, hell!' His head came down as he found her mouth again, his lips hot and demanding, bruising in their strength. Sarah shuddered, her whole body clenching in shocked reaction to the demanding assault before the shock faded just as abruptly and she kissed him back, her mouth giving all he demanded. When he parted her lips, she let him, let his tongue slide inside her mouth to seduce hers into a rhythm that sent quivering curls of hot sensation pouring through her. When his hand slid down from her face to skim lightly over the soft curves of her body, his fingers seemed to follow the trail of heat, follow it and deepen it until she felt as though she was on fire, burning with this need to have him kiss her, touch her and go on touching her until he assuaged the desire.

'James!' His name was so sweet on her lips, so sweet that she wanted to say it again and again just to savour the sound, but as his hand moved to cover her breast it was impossible. Sarah went quite still, waiting...for what? For the cruel touch she'd once suffered before, for the roughness that had terrified her?

Whatever her mind warned her to expect, it never happened. There was nothing rough about the way he stroked his palm across the soft curve of her breast, nothing cruel about the way his fingers gently found the small nipple and stroked it until it stood rigidly erect, swollen with desire to have him touch it again and again.

When he slid his hand under the hem of the sweatshirt and parted the buttons of her blouse to touch her breast through the thin cotton bra, she gasped with pleasure, unable to believe that such a light, almost gentle touch could cause such a raging storm of emotions inside her. She murmured softly, pulling his head down so that she could press kisses to his cheek, along the hard line of his jaw, and felt rather than saw him smile.

'And I thought you were repressed! How wrong can a person be?' There was just a faint mockery in that deeply beautiful voice, just the barest trace, aimed more at himself, but Sarah stiffened at once. What was she doing? What was she allowing him to do? They were alone in the middle of the night and she was all but handing him a written invitation to seduce her!

Shame flooded her and she tried to pull free of his hold, but he continued to hold her, his hand stilling on her breast.

'Let me go...please.' Her voice was filled with embarrassment, and she heard him curse softly half under his breath. His hand slid away from her breast, firm yet surprisingly gentle as he pulled the sweatshirt back into place, although he still didn't let her go. She could feel him watching her through the darkness, feel the hot touch of his eyes studying her pale, shamed face, and the desire she'd felt just moments before gave one sudden last surge before she ruthlessly suppressed it.

'We didn't do anything wrong, Sarah. Nothing for you to be ashamed of.' James's tone was soothing, gentler than she'd expected and far kinder than she deserved for leading him on like that, even though it had been unwittingly done.

'Didn't we?' She shrugged, sending the last of the pins spilling from her hair on to the floor so that it fell around her shoulders in a soft tangle of curls. 'I'm not experienced enough to judge that sort of behaviour, I'm afraid.'

'No? You seemed to be managing extremely well to me.' There was a teasing lightness to the response that she missed, too full of shame to understand that he was trying to put her at ease.

'Well, I'm sorry if I gave you that impression. I should have realised that you'd always imagine the worst of me, though, shouldn't I?' Her laugh was bitter. 'Next thing you'll be accusing me of trying to seduce you!'

'I doubt that. I may have my faults, Sarah, but not owning up to my actions isn't one of them. I kissed you just now because I wanted to, because I couldn't think of anything in the world I wanted to do more.' He caught a handful of her soft hair and tugged on it so that she was forced to meet his eyes as he snapped on the light. 'I wanted you, Sarah, in every way that implies, and if you hadn't had the sense to stop me then you and I would be making love right now!'

'I... James... I...' Sarah didn't know what to say, couldn't find words to deny the obvious truth of the statement. If she hadn't abruptly come to her senses then she and James would have...

Her eyelids fluttered closed, her face going pale and still in the soft light, her body aching with a sense of loss that was more shocking than anything. She had never imagined that she could want a man as she had wanted him!

'You wanted me, didn't you, Sarah?'

Had he read her mind? She had no idea, but she couldn't lie, even though common sense told her it was every sort of madness to admit it to him. 'Yes.'

He sighed, his fingers stroking deliberately across her mouth which was still swollen from the kisses they had shared. 'Yes, I expect that's one of the reasons we argue so much. Sexual attraction is a powerful emotion to handle.'

What was he saying? Was he really admitting that he was attracted to her that way? The shock must have shown on her face, because he smiled coldly, his eyes devoid of any warmth.

'I see that surprises you, Sarah. That I should feel that way about you.' He skimmed a hard glance over her still figure. 'It surprises me too. You're nothing like the kind of woman I usually take to bed to appease my appetites!'

Her face flamed at the cruel mockery, and she stared at him in silence, unable to hide her hurt. It was obvious that a man as attractive as he would have women friends, but to have them thrust into her face like this was more than she could bear.

'What, no comment to make? Why, Sarah? Have I offended your maidenly modesty by talking of such things?' He shook his head so that a lock of dark hair fell on to his broad forehead, giving him a rakish air. 'I wonder if I misjudged that modesty, though? I remember accusing you of making a play for me once, and now I wonder if I was that far off the track. You responded to me just now with anything but maidenly modesty, didn't you, my sweet?'

Why was he suddenly being so cruel? Why was he using that cool, hard tone to whip her with and make her face up to what a fool she'd been? Sarah stared back at him for one long moment, then drew in a slow, silent breath as the last of the magic faded, as she should have known it would. Her life had been lacking in any sort of magic for years, so she'd been a fool to think that it would change.

'I can't change the way you think, James, so I won't waste time in trying to do so. You can attribute my response to anything you choose, but I doubt if you'd be right.'

Her own voice echoed his coldness, and anger flickered in the depths of his eyes before he smiled grimly. '*Touché*, Sarah! You're turning out to be far different from what I imagined when we set out on this trip.'

'Really?' She smoothed the tangle of curls back from her face, twisting the thick length into a plait, glad to see that her hands were quite steady as she worked on weaving the strands into place.

'Mmm, very different. There are hidden depths in you, Sarah Marshall, and I don't just mean that dark secret you seem so determined to keep to yourself. It makes me wonder what it would be like to dig deeper.' His eyes slid to her mouth, lingering there in a blatant look that she felt to her very depths before he looked back straight into her eyes. 'There's passion in you, Sarah, a passion that I suspect has never been truly aroused before. It's a challenge few men could resist.'

Fear curled inside her, sharp and cold, but she fought it down. 'If by that you mean that you intend to be the one to arouse it then don't bother. I'm not in the market for a lover, thank you very much!'

'No?' With a speed that shocked her he reached across the gap and caught her arm to pull her closer to him. 'I think that's exactly what you do need—a lover to awake you from that sham of a life you lead.' He lifted his hand and touched her mouth again, parting her lips so that he could run the tip of his finger across the inner softness in a caress that sent hot little spirals of sensation curling through her. 'You're more than ready to take a man into your life and into your bed, Sarah Marshall, and it's about time you owned up to the fact.'

'How dare you?' She dragged herself away, pushing his hand aside as she sank back into her seat again. 'I don't need you or anyone telling me how to run my private life!'

'That's where you're wrong. You need someone to wake you up to what you're doing by living this way before it's too late. Is this really what you want for yourself, Sarah? This lonely, sterile existence? You're not frigid—we've established that tonight, if nothing else. You just have to admit that you need love as much as any other woman does.'

'Love? Or sex? That's really what you mean! You think I should jump into bed with some man or other to get rid of my hang-ups!' Sarah laughed at the bitter irony, then bit her lip before the laughter could turn to hysteria. 'Well, if that was an offer then I'm afraid the answer is no...thank you! I don't need any of your kind of therapy!'

'I wasn't offering, merely making an observation. I admit that I feel a certain attraction to you, but I like my women to come without strings attached, and you, sweet Sarah, have so many strings binding you that it would take a lifetime to cut through them.' He shrugged lightly. 'However, if you do ever manage to get yourself straightened out then make sure you give me a call. I have a feeling that you and I could scale to dizzying heights together in bed.'

'I wouldn't call you if you were the last man left alive on earth, James MacAllister! Is that clear? Never!'

She turned her back on him, huddling against the door, her face colouring hectically as she heard him mutter something softly under his breath, something that sounded suspiciously along the lines of, '"The lady doth protest too much, methinks."' She shut her mouth on the sharp retort, closing her eyes and pretending to sleep, but long after James's breathing had settled into a steady rhythm she was still awake, his words echoing mockingly inside her head.

For those brief, almost magical minutes when he had held her and kissed her, she'd given no thought to what was sensible or what was foolish, nor even to what had happened in the past. He had kissed her, and she'd responded as though she had been waiting for that moment all her life.

CHAPTER EIGHT

THE mist was lifting, allowing the sun to filter through and dress the countryside in pale golden rays. Sarah stopped to catch her breath, brushing the mist-dampened wisps of hair from her face as she watched a small village start to appear in the distance as if by magic as the white shroud faded away.

They had been walking for well over an hour now, and if they were aiming for that village then they must still have some way to go. Traffic had started to flow along the road now, one of several such roads that had been built to open up the formerly impenetrable mountain range which divided France from Spain, but, although James had made several attempts to flag a passing car down and ask for help, none had stopped.

James. The name slid past the conscious barrier she had built in her mind during the long, sleepless night, and she turned to look at him, experiencing again that strange aching sense of loss she'd felt before. With his dark hair spangled with drops of moisture and his tanned skin gleaming damply in the soft light he looked so devastatingly handsome that she felt her heart lurch in instant response, felt the fragile barrier start to crumble.

He must have sensed her watching him, because he turned, a fleeting unguarded expression in his dark eyes that made her breath catch, but then he blanked it out with an easy deliberation that made her go cold. If she was to learn anything at all from the bitter experience last night then it was to expect nothing from James MacAllister at all.

'Ready to go on?' His tone was coolly impersonal; they could have been two strangers who had been forced to make this journey rather than two people who had shared those moments of passion in the car, and something inside Sarah flared to angry life.

'Yes!' There was no mistaking the snap in her reply, no mistaking the angry glitter that showed in the depths of her eyes, but although James gave her a searching look he said nothing. Sarah bit her lip, walking past him to lead the way along the road, hating herself for wanting to make him acknowledge what had happened between them and hating him even more for refusing to do so. He couldn't have made his feelings for her any plainer by that obvious refusal.

'Wait!' He snapped the order at her, his hand catching hers as he pulled her back on to the rough grass which edged the road. Sarah pulled her hand away from his, feeling her fingers tingling from the brief contact.

'What's the matter?' she demanded curtly, refusing to look at him as she stared along the road the way they'd come.

'I think I can hear something coming. Sounds louder than a car, maybe a truck. Perhaps the driver will be more willing to help than all those cars who've passed us.' He glanced down at her, his face tightening as he saw the way she was staring past him. 'Wait there, and for heaven's sake don't go running into the road the way you did last night!'

She couldn't help herself, couldn't stop the words even though the minute she said them she regretted it. 'Don't worry, I might be the teacher, but I'm still capable of learning a lesson, and I won't forget anything I learned last night!'

Anger flashed across James's face as he heard the sarcasm in her voice, but before he could say anything a lorry appeared out of the mist, driving steadily towards them. Without a word James stepped into the road, waving his arms to flag it down, leaving Sarah to catch her breath and wish she'd never spoken so impulsively. He might have said nothing, but then again he hadn't needed to. His expression had said it all for him, and she went cold with dread as she wondered what shape his retribution would take later when they were alone!

Forced either to stop or run James down, the vehicle ground to a halt with a squeal of brakes. The driver wound his window down, obviously none too pleased at having been stopped that way.

'Come on. Tell him what's happened and ask if he'll give us a lift into the nearest town.' With a complete lack of finesse, James caught Sarah's arm and steered her towards the lorry, waiting impatiently as she explained their predicament. 'Well? What does he say?'

Sarah barely glanced at him, smoothing her hair back from her damp face. 'That he's only going to the village, but that we can have a lift there if it will help.'

'Good. At last something's going right for a change!' There was no disguising James's impatience as he opened the cab door and helped her up the steep step, his hands firm around her hips as he boosted her the rest of the way. Sarah scrambled into the cab, her face colouring as she saw the appreciative glance the driver gave her slender thighs where the skirt had slipped upwards. Hurriedly she pulled it down to her knees, then scooted over on the seat as James climbed in beside her, his long legs brushing against hers as he eased himself into the small space left on the bench seat. Sarah tried to edge over a fraction to give him more room and escape the disturbing pressure of his thigh against hers, but there was little leeway with three of them squashed into the small cab. When the lorry started up with a shuddering jolt, she slipped sideways into James and stiffened at once, reacting instinctively to the touch of his body.

'For heaven's sake! I don't bite, woman.'

'No?' There was a tartness to the single word that she hadn't intended and which he didn't miss. He smiled suddenly, his mouth curving wickedly in a way that made her heart do a crazy little shudder.

'No, I don't. Or at least not in *that* way!' His eyes skimmed over her in a lingering look that she felt in every shaken inch before coming back to meet hers with laughter in their depths and something else, something that did little to quell the foolish quiver of awareness that was racing through her. 'I must admit that if the circumstances were right I could be tempted to... if you understand what I mean?'

Was that seductive note in his deep voice deliberate? Of course it was! Deliberate and practised and completely aware of the effect it would have. James was far from being a monk; he must be well aware of the effect he could have on a woman using that sexy tone!

Sarah glared at him, but he seemed unperturbed by her obvious annoyance as he slid his arm along the back of the seat so that his fingers just brushed against her neck. She wriggled away, then murmured a hasty apology as she bumped into the driver. Compressing her lips into a thin line, she sat and stared straight ahead, not even sparing James a glance when he bent towards her.

'Not sulking, are you, Sarah? I never imagined you'd resort to that sort of childish behaviour.'

'I wouldn't dream of sulking!' she snapped back. 'If anyone's being childish then it's you. I don't intend to start playing any more of your silly games this morning, but that doesn't mean I'm sulking!'

'Silly games? Well, well!' His eyebrows rose until they disappeared under the silky dark hair falling across his brow.

'And what does that mean? Look here, James, if you imagine I'm going to let you throw last night into my face at every turn then you can think again.' Hectic colour tinged her face as the memories of last night rushed back. She bit her lip, feeling again the delicate yet devastating touch of his fingers on her breast, the hungry demand of his mouth on hers. For a moment they stared at each other in silence, and Sarah felt her heart stop as she saw an echo of everything she was feeling cross his face, then abruptly he turned away.

'I wasn't the one who brought it up in the first place. However, I agree that it would be better if it was forgotten. No one likes to be reminded of a momentary lapse.'

The coldness was back with a vengeance, chilling her to the bone. Sarah shrank away from him, wounded beyond belief by the cutting, dismissive statement. Was that how he saw it, as a momentary lapse? Last night he had said he had wanted her, but had that been the truth? Had it been more a case that he had wanted a woman and that she had been conveniently handy when the desire had struck?

The pain she felt was so sharp that it seemed to numb her whole body, so that it was a moment before she realised that the driver was speaking to her. Forcing herself to concentrate, she answered his questions about what had happened to their car, centring her whole attention on him so that she could ignore James, who was sitting silently staring at the passing countryside. The man seemed to blossom under the whole-hearted attention Sarah paid him, soon monopolising the conversation as he explained where his job had taken him driving throughout France. Sarah was glad that he seemed not to need much of a response from her apart from a few murmured comments. Frankly, she wasn't feeling up to making much intelligent conversation.

When the lorry came to a slow halt in the village, she smiled at the driver in relief, unaware that the smile held more warmth than she would normally have afforded to a stranger. He jumped from the cab, holding his hands up to help her down, lifting her with an easy show of strength from the high step of the cab before almost reluctantly letting her feet touch the ground.

'When you're quite ready then may I suggest we try to find a garage and get someone out to the car?' There was an unpleasant ring to James's deep voice as he came round to stand beside her, and Sarah took an instant dislike to the tone. Ignoring his hard-eyed stare, she turned back to the driver, repeating her effusive thanks. The man smiled, his eyes sliding over her slim figure in a way that made Sarah feel suddenly uncomfortable. Hurriedly she turned back to James—then stared round in surprise when she could see no sign of him. Where on earth had he gone?

She looked round in concern, then suddenly spotted him crossing the square, his long legs eating up the distance. She ran after him, panting as she tried to catch up, but he carried on walking despite the fact that she called his name several times.

'Why didn't you wait? I wondered where you'd gone.' She smoothed her hair back from her face, glaring at him as she slewed to a halt, but he barely spared her a glance as he strode on.

'Wait? What for? You to finish off making eyes at Romeo back there?' He smiled nastily, his eyes glacial as they settled on her flushed face. 'You're full of surprises, Sarah. I just didn't realise that you were so man-hungry you'd start trying to pick men up at every opportunity.'

'Man-hungry? Me? Why, you...you...' She gripped his arm and stopped him from walking on, her face filled with fury as she met that cold, scornful stare. 'How dare you say such a thing? You have no grounds whatsoever for making such an accusation!'

'No?' James cast a meaningful look over his shoulder, then looked back at her. 'That was the impression you gave me, and, from the look of it, the one you gave to loverboy back there.'

Sarah looked back, her heart sinking as she saw that the driver was still watching them. Perhaps she had been a trifle more friendly than usual towards the man, but that didn't give James the right to accuse her of what he had! 'Don't be ridiculous! I was just being polite, that's all; thanking him for stopping. After all, it was good of him to do so.'

James shrugged lightly, the muscles in his arm under her fingers flexing in a way that she found strangely disturbing. 'There's polite and polite. I'm sure you must know what I mean, Sarah. However, what you do is your business when it doesn't affect me in any way. You can make a play for any guy you meet, but not right now when there are more pressing matters to attend to. We still have to sort out the car and find Catherine. Perhaps you can manage to keep your baser instincts under control long enough for us to achieve that!'

Oh, if she were a man she'd hit him! Hit him hard on that arrogant jaw and wipe that belittling smile off his face! Sarah ground her teeth in fury, clenching her fists at her sides, knowing it would be a mistake to even think of resorting to any sort of physical violence with a man like James MacAllister. He lived by no one's rules apart from his own and would probably think nothing of hitting her back!

In silent seething fury, she let her hand fall from his arm and trailed after him across the square, thinking up ways of paying him back, each one more fanciful than the first. Boiling in oil, hanged, drawn and quartered, thrown into a...

She cannoned into the back of him when he stopped, colour surging into her face when she saw the speculative look he gave her.

'I'm sure you'd end up in prison if you attempted any of the things you're conjuring up, so may I suggest that you forget about getting even with me and concentrate on the reason why we're here?' He nodded towards the cluttered forecourt of the garage, ignoring her gasp of shock that he should have guessed so accurately what had been running through her head. 'Can you explain about the car to them, and see if they'll go and fetch it in to be repaired? We need to get on our way just as soon as we can.'

Sarah nodded, averting her face from his too knowing gaze as she hurried into the garage. How had he realised what she was thinking just now? She had no idea, but she would be careful not to make such a mistake in future. She was already more vulnerable with him than she liked to be; if he got even an inkling of some of the things that had passed through her mind recently then she'd be lost!

He was standing leaning against the side-wall of the garage when she came out, his long legs loosely crossed at the ankle, his eyes closed as he tilted his face up to the strengthening rays of the sun. Just for a moment Sarah hesitated, studying the hard, clear lines of his profile, the way the sun reflected off his dark hair and glinted on the wings of silver at his temples. With the thin cotton jeans clinging to his long legs, and the chunky thick-knit sweater bulking his muscular torso, he looked big and strong and indomitable as he stood there. It was only when he opened his eyes and she saw the stark worry etched in their depths that Sarah felt her anger fade.

'We'll find her, James,' she said softly, walking over to stand in front of him and stare quietly up into his face. 'Catherine is a sensible girl. She won't do anything stupid.'

'Won't she?' Just for a moment it was almost as though he was seeking reassurance, then he straightened abruptly, pushing his hair back with an impatient sweep of his hand. 'Forgive me if I don't find your opinion that comforting. From what I've learned so far your judgement isn't worth a whole lot.'

The sarcasm hurt, but Sarah had become adept over the years at hiding her true feelings. She stared calmly back at him, betraying nothing of the pain his words invoked. 'Maybe it isn't, but I think I can safely say that I know far more about how Catherine thinks lately than you do.'

'Is that so? Then explain to me exactly why you failed to see what was apparently going on right under your nose in the hotel.' He smiled grimly. 'If I were in your shoes, Miss Marshall, I'd be asking myself whether or not I was fit to be in charge of children. I doubt if you have any idea what passes through their minds, so don't kid yourself that Catherine is any different. However, I really am not interested in your attempts to comfort me. All I want to know is how long it will take to get the car brought back here and repaired. I take it you did manage to sort that out as requested?'

'Of course.' It shouldn't have hurt to bear the brunt of his anger and fear. She knew his opinion of her, he'd made no secret of it from the outset, but each harsh word was like another wound piercing her heart. Why? Why should it hurt so much that he should hate her so?

'Then if it isn't too much trouble can you tell me what's going on?'

She took a slow breath, letting the answer that was hovering at the back of her mind fade into obscurity with a strange feeling of relief, suddenly afraid to face the truth. 'They'll go out and collect the car as soon as they can. Assuming that it's the sump that's damaged then it will be late afternoon before it's fixed. That's the best they can do.'

'Damnation! More delay!' James hit one clenched fist against his palm, impatience in every taut line. 'I don't suppose you thought to ask if there's another car available that we could hire?'

'That's where you're wrong. I did ask, but unfortunately the village isn't big enough to have much demand for hire cars. It seems that we're stuck here until our car's mended.'

'Evidently so.' He pushed away from the wall, glancing round the quiet square. 'Looks as if your stupidity has caused us yet more problems, doesn't it?'

Tears stung at her eyes and she turned her head away so that he wouldn't see them. 'I don't suppose it's any use saying I'm sorry?'

'None at all. It won't achieve anything. Let's just hope and pray that the car can be fixed by the afternoon, then at least we shall be able to put an end to this farce by the evening.' James skimmed her averted face with a hard look, and if he saw the tears glittering on her lashes they did little to soften his attitude. Indeed, if the tone of his deep voice was any measure to go by, they just seemed to anger him even more. 'Believe me, Sarah, I shall be glad when this is over and done with and you and I can go our separate ways.'

What could she say? Admit that she was dreading the moment when they would part? If she told him that he would probably laugh in her face and accuse her of something worse than he had accused her of already.

It was pride that held her together, pride and a determination not to let him see how she felt. 'No gladder than I shall be, believe me. It's obvious that you and I have nothing in common.'

'Nothing? Oh, I wouldn't quite say that.' His gaze slid to her mouth, lingering there quite deliberately in a way that Sarah knew was meant to punish, yet she couldn't help the quaking shudder which ran through her as she felt the look. Abruptly she turned away and walked back across the square, barely aware of what she was doing or where she was going, only knowing that she had to get away from James MacAllister before she committed the biggest folly of all and let him see how much she wanted to feel again his hard mouth on hers!

Sun glinted off the leaves, casting lacy shadows on to the dusty ground. Sarah leant back in the chair and sipped her cooling coffee, watching James as he bent to take his turn in the leisurely game of boule. There was a roar of appreciation and a spattering of clapping as he took the highest score. He smiled round at the rest of the men and shook several by the hand, then came back to the table and dropped down into a chair, looking more relaxed than Sarah had ever seen him before.

'I take it that you won?' she asked lightly, sipping the coffee before setting the small cup down.

He shook his head, picking up the glass of pastis and taking a drink of the aniseed-flavoured liquid before answering. 'No chance. Those men are experts—I wouldn't have a chance of beating them. That last turn was just a lucky one, a fluke.'

Sarah glanced back across the square, watching the men as they gathered up the boules and carried them over to a table while they too enjoyed the afternoon ritual of chatting over a few glasses of pastis. 'I suppose not. You were honoured that they invited you to join in in the first place. The French are usually rather reserved with strangers.' Her gaze moved back to where he sat easily in the straight-backed wooden chair, cradling the half-full glass. 'You have a knack of making yourself at home, it seems.'

'Honed to perfection over many years spent travelling.' He must have seen her interest, because he smiled as he set the glass down and stretched so that every muscle under the thin grey shirt rippled disconcertingly.

Sarah licked her suddenly parched lips, forcing herself to concentrate on the conversation to keep her mind from wandering in directions she was sure it wasn't meant to go. 'You've mentioned that you travel a great deal before, yet I've never fully understood why. Catherine told me you were an architect, and I've seen for myself examples of your work. It's good.' She blushed suddenly, realising that must sound as though she'd gone out of her way to study his work. However, he didn't pick her up on that as she'd feared he would.

'That's so, but I've been working with an overseas development agency for the last few years, offering advice on low-cost housing.' He shrugged, staring across the square, yet she had the feeling that he was miles away. 'It's been challenging work, disturbing at times too when you're confronted by the poverty that exists in some countries. I've been fortunate in my career and made more than enough money to allow me to take on the project when it was put to me.'

'And will you continue with it once Catherine is found?'

'No. I'd already decided that I'd done all I could and that it was time for someone else to take over. Don't get me wrong, I gained as much from the experience as I gave, but you have to move on, and that's what I intend to do now—move on to the next phase of my life and look to the future.'

They were only talking for the sake of politeness, filling in time until the car was ready, yet suddenly Sarah felt overwhelmed with sadness that she would never be a part of that future he mentioned. Shaken by the thought, she stood up abruptly, knocking against the table in her haste so that the coffee-cup rattled in its saucer. 'I... I'll just go and check on the car. It should be nearly ready by now.'

She started past him, stopping when his fingers linked loosely around her wrist. Under his hand her pulse leapt in an instant response she knew he'd felt, but there was little she could do.

'Running away, Sarah? Does talking about the future disturb you, then?'

'Of course not.' She gave a strained little laugh that did more to betray her feelings than disguise them. 'I just thought I'd better check on the car. Is that a problem?'

'No.' His hand moved, his fingers encircling her wrist before smoothing up and down the soft skin of her inner arm in a rhythm that sent tingles of sweet sensation racing through her. 'The only problem is yours—the fact that you won't face up to the kind of future you'll have.'

'I don't remember discussing *my* future plans, James! It was your future we were talking about, wasn't it?'

'It was indeed, and our two paths aren't destined to cross again once this mess is sorted out.' He let her wrist go. 'Naturally, I shall be removing Catherine from your school after what's happened. So once we part, Sarah, that will be that. We most probably won't meet again.'

'Well, that day can't come fast enough for me!' She turned and walked away, willing herself to believe that what she'd said was the truth, but deep in her heart she knew it was just a lie. The thought of never seeing James again made her want to sit down and cry.

CHAPTER NINE

'WHAT do you mean, it won't be ready today? Damn it, Sarah, we need that car now, not tomorrow!'

Fury echoed in James's voice, and Sarah sighed, wishing she weren't the one who had to break the bad news to him. In olden days a messenger bearing unwelcome news had often been killed for his pains, and now she had some inkling about how they'd felt! The look on James's face was enough to stop a man dead in his tracks without him having to resort to other means.

'I know we do, but that doesn't change the fact that it won't be ready until then. Evidently there was something else damaged, and the man at the garage will have to send out to Luchon for the parts.'

'I don't believe this. I really and truly don't believe this is happening!' James walked a few steps away from her, tension evident in every strong line of his lean body before he swung round. 'How about them giving us a lift into Luchon? That way we can hire another car and carry on.'

It was an idea, and one Sarah dearly wished she'd thought of sooner. She shook her head, avoiding his hard-eyed stare, waiting for the full weight of his wrath to fall on her as it always seemed to do. 'I'm afraid he's already left. We're too late to go with him.'

With a magnificent show of restraint he managed to say nothing, just turned away and walked back across the square, leaving her to trail miserably after him. The atmosphere had been tense between them all afternoon, and now it could only get worse. It was blatantly obvious that James didn't want to spend any more time in her company than he was forced to, and now it seemed that would be even more than anticipated.

He stopped outside the small café where they had lunched and turned to stare round the quiet square with its few streets leading from it. 'I suppose we shall have to spend the night here, then, from the look of it. Have you any idea if there's an inn or somewhere to stay?'

Sarah shook her head, the last rays from the sun settling a golden cast on her light brown hair. 'No, I'm afraid not. I'll go inside and ask.'

'Do that—and while you're at it see if there's a telephone I can use. Maybe I can find a firm willing to bring a car out here to us. Hell and damnation! I can't believe something else could go wrong to add to the list.'

There was little she could say apart from apologise again, and frankly she'd made enough apologies recently to last her a lifetime! Without another word, she hurried inside, her heart sinking even further when the proprietress informed her that not only was there no inn in the village but that a recent storm had brought the telephone lines down and they still hadn't been repaired. She could only imagine James's reaction to that bit of news!

'Well?' He had followed her inside, leaning against the counter with his arms folded across his chest as he waited to hear the good news. Sarah took a deep breath, then steeled herself to tell him, stopping when the woman continued eagerly. She blushed crimson and shook her head, then jumped when James caught her arm.

'What's she saying? Did I catch something about a room being available here?'

Sarah shook her head again, looking anywhere but at him. 'No.'

'Why do I get the feeling that you're lying, my sweet?' He smiled at her, his lips curling tauntingly before he turned his attention to the woman behind the counter, speaking with the slow deliberation of one unaccustomed to speaking in another language. Sarah stared aloofly in front of her, making no attempt to help him out in his painfully slow questioning. It didn't matter what he asked or what answer he got, the whole idea was impossible!

'Tut, tut, Sarah, so you were lying! I'm surprised at you.' With one last charming smile at the proprietress, he slid his hand under Sarah's elbow and half led, half dragged her out into the street.

'Let me go.' She shook him off, glaring back at him, hating the mocking expression on his arrogant face. 'All right, so I lied, but it makes no difference to our situation, does it? There's only one room above the café, and if you imagine I'd be willing to share it with you then you're mad!'

'Then what do you intend to do? Spend the night out here?' James shivered dramatically as he cast a look up at the sky. 'Remember how cold it goes at night, Sarah? I don't think you'll find it at all comfortable, but if that's the way you want it then who am I to object?'

'You'd really do that? Leave me out here alone all night while you're snugly ensconced in that room?'

'What else do you suggest? That I should offer to let you have the room all to yourself and spend the night out here instead?' He shook his head, his expression one of derision. 'Wake up, Sarah! This is the 1990s, the time of equality between the sexes. I don't feel the least obliged to do that when you're at liberty to share the room with me. We spent last night together in the car, so why should this be any different?'

Why indeed? Apart from the fact that sharing a bedroom was markedly more intimate than being forced to share the car... and look what had happened between them then!

With a toss of her head, Sarah turned away, ignoring the mocking wave James gave her as he disappeared inside the café. She walked along the quiet street, stopping when she came to the wood that marked the end of the village. The wind was starting to rise again as it had done the previous night, taking the warmth out of the air. She wrapped her arms around her, tucking her hands into the sleeves of the sweater as she stood watching the way the trees tossed restlessly in the rising currents of air, then turned and looked back at the café, wondering what on earth she was going to do to get through the night. Frankly, the thought of spending it outside was daunting, but what was the alternative? Agreeing to share that room with James?

No way!

The room was dark and quiet, just the dim glow from the lamp lighting the shadows. Sarah lay in bed staring blankly at the ceiling, studying the cracks that ran through the white-painted plaster. Outside it had just started to rain, the soft beating of raindrops on the window-pane barely disturbing the silence. She was warm and cosy, yet she couldn't sleep, and her insomnia owed nothing whatsoever to any fear of a repeat of the nightmare. This time it was all down to James!

She tossed back the blankets and walked over to the window, rubbing her hand across the glass when it misted with the heat of her breath as she peered out. There wasn't much to see, though, apart from a few lights across the square, but her gaze didn't rest on them but on something closer, on the glowing tip of a cigarette being smoked by someone sitting at one of the tables.

Anger and guilt ran through her in almost equal measure and she sighed as she turned away to drag on her robe. She should have realised that that unscrupulous man was up to something when he'd suddenly offered quite out of the blue to let *her* have the room. She'd known his views all along, but somehow she'd allowed him to lull her into a false sense of security with a good meal and a couple of glasses of the rough local wine. She'd actually thanked him for being so chivalrous as to make the offer! Well, chivalry be damned! He must have known she'd feel guilty as hell and give in. Damn the man, he was far too clever by half!

She left the room and ran quietly downstairs, muttering under her breath when the bell on the café door tinkled noisily as she drew the bolts. Shooting a quick glance over her shoulder to check that she'd not disturbed anyone, she hurried out into the rain, shivering as she stepped into a puddle at the bottom of the steps.

'Mmm, took you longer than I'd anticipated. You must be tougher than you look, sweet Sarah.' James grinned at her, leaning back in the chair, his dark hair plastered to his head, the rain-soaked shirt moulding every perfect muscle in his chest and shoulders. Sarah bit back the desire to sigh with pure appreciation at the sight he made sitting there looking so totally masculine, and whipped up her anger instead.

'If I weren't afraid that Madame St Clair would end up by coming down to fetch you in I'd be happy to let you stay out here all night! I just didn't want to cause her any more trouble after she's been so kind in offering us a room.'

'Of course. I should have realised that, shouldn't I? I shall consider myself suitably chastised for imagining anything else. Now shall we go inside?' He stood up and walked over to the door, holding it with a mocking courtesy for her to precede him inside, making Sarah rue the fact that she'd been so soft-hearted.

She glared at him as she marched back inside. 'You knew I wouldn't be able to leave you out here all night, didn't you? That's why you offered to let me have the room.'

He shrugged lightly, closing the door. 'Let's just say it was a calculated risk.' He smiled suddenly, his eyes filled with laughter. 'I'm only glad it paid off. Another few minutes out there and I'd have been forced to admit defeat and throw myself on your mercy. I'm half-frozen as it is—feel.'

He ran his fingers down her cheek, letting her feel the coldness of his flesh, and Sarah shivered. She drew back at once, hating the way her heart had started to hammer crazily at the first touch of his hand. 'You only have yourself to blame. You made the offer, I didn't ask.'

'Of course. I knew damned well you would never have given in without making all kinds of a fuss about it. This seemed the easiest way to avoid all that. It might be old-fashioned, Sarah, but in my view a woman needs protecting, and there's no way I'd have allowed you to stay out there by yourself!'

He turned away after that arrogant assertion, his long legs carrying him swiftly up the stairs. Sarah followed more slowly, wondering why it was that she felt so guilty. It had been James who had set out to trick her, yet she felt as though she was the one at fault for suggesting that he should leave her outside.

Still pondering on it, she walked into the bedroom—and stopped dead, feeling colour suffusing her face as she saw him standing at the side of the old-fashioned double bed. In a fast sweep her eyes ran from the top of his dark, damp head to the tips of his well-shaped feet before she turned away with a muttered apology.

'Don't worry—I'm ready.' He flipped the bedclothes back and slid between the sheets, folding the blanket back to his waist. Sarah's eyes seemed to have a will of their own as they slid back to the muscular contours of his tanned chest with its covering of thick black hair before she forced them away.

'Don't you have any pyjamas to wear? Surely you don't intend to sleep in those... those...'

'Shorts?' he suggested almost helpfully, but one quick look at the mockery on his face told her that being helpful wasn't his intention.

'Yes!' she snapped. 'Shorts.'

James held his hands out palm upwards in a gesture of contrition. 'Sorry, but I never use them. I've never had much cause to before, in fact.'

Meaning that the women he usually shared a bed with preferred him dressed just as he was...or in less! The wave of jealousy that swept through her startled her so much that she stood frozen for a long moment, and James seemed to misinterpret her hesitation. He tossed back the blankets and slid his legs out of the bed, his face stony. 'I should have realised it was too much to expect you to behave sensibly, Sarah. I think I prefer to take my chances outside in the rain than face another of your semi-hysterical outbursts.'

He started to drag his trousers back on over the dark boxer shorts, muttering when the wet fabric stuck to his skin, and abruptly she awoke from her trance. 'You won't have to,' she said with quiet dignity. 'I'm sorry, I'm just not used to this sort of situation. However, we're both adults, James, and I'm sure we can handle it.'

She slipped off the robe and slid into bed, avoiding his searching gaze as she pulled the blankets up to her chin. There was silence, then the quick dip of the mattress as he climbed in beside her. Sarah screwed her eyes tightly shut, trying her hardest not to remember what had happened the previous night, but when James switched off the lamp to plunge the room into darkness every sense seemed to flare into life.

Was it just imagination, or could she actually feel the heat from his body flowing towards her, could she actually hear the sound of his heart beating, really smell that faint tantalising aroma of his skin? When he moved suddenly, making himself more comfortable, she jumped and half rose from the bed, ready to run.

'Sarah! We went through all this fiasco last night, didn't we?' He sat up, looming over her in the darkness, his eyes flashing with annoyance.

'Yes, and look what almost happened then!' Oh, why had she said that? She wanted to forget about it, not refresh his memory!

'Almost, don't forget. Nothing really happened, you little idiot.' James lay back, drawing her down to cushion her head in the hollow of his shoulder. 'I promise I won't do anything you don't want me to, so go to sleep.'

'With you holding me like this?' She wriggled, trying to free herself, and heard him laugh softly.

'Which is worse? Lying there jumping every time I move a muscle or lying in my arms and knowing exactly what I'm up to? Come on, Sarah, be sensible about this and go to sleep. It'll be morning before you realise it.' He eased her more comfortably against him, his touch quite impersonal despite the intimacy of their situation. Sarah sighed softly, knowing she was being a fool. Her breath stirred the hairs on his chest so that they tickled her cheek, and unthinkingly she smoothed them down, feeling their springiness under her fingertips, and found her hand lingering for a moment on the warm, firm muscles.

'See, I don't bite. Relax. Go to sleep. You're quite safe.' He covered her hand with his, pressing her fingers lightly against his body in a contact she knew she should resist yet didn't. He had tricked her, mocked her, poured scorn upon her at each and every turn, yet suddenly she knew she could trust him to keep his word. She was quite safe, and she slept.

It was a dream that woke her. Not the nightmare this time, but a dream that was so erotically sensual it startled her awake.

She lay still, feeling the hot blood swirling through her veins, then tried to ease herself out of James's arms, embarrassed by the vividness of the images that had filled her mind.

He murmured and drew her closer, one long hair-roughened leg trapping hers so that she was brought into intimate contact with the lower part of his body, and she froze, every bit of her growing tense, and somehow that tension must have communicated itself to him.

His hand smoothed down her side, following the dip of her waist, the flare of her hip before it came to rest on the smoothness of her thigh where the prim cotton gown had ridden up. Slowly his fingers roamed over the bare flesh, down, then up, sliding under the hem of the gown, and Sarah gasped. She had no idea if he was asleep or coming awake, but what she did know was that that touch was growing too intimately disturbing by the second!

She pulled away from him abruptly, dragging herself from the warm shelter of his arms, and rolled over on to her side, shivering at the coolness of the sheets as she balanced on the very edge of the mattress.

'You'll fall out of this bed if you lie like that. Come back here, Sarah.'

So he was awake, very much so, despite the husky sleep-roughened note in his deep voice! Sarah rolled over and glowered at him through the darkness, wishing there were some way to erase the erotic perfection of all those shocking dreams from her mind.

'And have you start playing your games again? No, thanks!'

'I wasn't playing any games, Sarah. I just woke up to find a warm and beautiful woman in my arms and acted accordingly.'

It hurt that he should admit that it could have been any woman in his arms, not just her. 'Well, I'm sorry to inform you, Mr MacAllister, that I have no intention of providing an outlet for your urges. If you're having problems along those lines, may I suggest that you go find yourself a woman who's willing to play "games" with you once we go our separate ways?'

'You sound so cross, Sarah, but that wasn't the way you sounded a few minutes ago when you were whispering my name.' He moved suddenly, drawing her back into the hard strength of his arms as he tilted her face to his. 'What were you dreaming about, my sweet little innocent? How it would feel to lie in my arms while we made love . . . hot, delicious love?'

His lips brushed across hers so lightly, yet the soft kiss seemed to fan the hot flames of desire, and she shuddered as she tried to draw away. 'No! Don't be silly. I wasn't dreaming about you.'

'The same as I wasn't dreaming about you too?' His hands slid down her spine, his fingers tracing every delicate ridge. 'I woke up with the thought of you in my head and the feel of you in my arms, Sarah, and the reality is even better than anything imagination could spin.'

'James!' Was it shock that made her voice so whispery, made the sound of his name sound more like an invitation than an objection? She had no idea, but just hearing it made her tremble. She was so vulnerable to him, even more so now after that startling admission.

'Sarah.' He said her name softly, no mockery in the deepness of his voice, just an ache of need that made everything womanly flare to sudden life. 'Maybe I should pretend about how I feel, but what's the point in denying it? I want you, Sarah. I want to hold you, kiss you, love you, act out all those wonderful pictures that have been driving me crazy for the past few hours, but I gave you my promise that you'd be safe, and I won't break it now. I won't try to take anything that you aren't willing to give.'

'Men always take, that's their nature.' She couldn't help the bitter note that welled so suddenly in her voice.

James shook his head, his face no more than a soft blur in the darkness. 'That's not true. Don't judge all men by one bad experience. That's the trouble, isn't it? You were hurt badly at some time in the past, and that's coloured your view of relationships. I don't know who he was or what happened, but all I can say is that if you continue to allow it to rule your life then he's won. He's made you an emotional cripple.'

It had never struck her that way before. Now just that one statement seemed to tear the veil from her eyes. She'd been crippled by the past for so long, living her life always afraid. She could never change what had happened, could never erase it completely from her life, but she had to put it behind her.

'Give and take is part of any relationship, Sarah,' he continued quietly when she didn't speak. 'But it doesn't have to be the woman who always gives and the man who always takes. It has to work both ways so that each finds pleasure from the act. I want you, Sarah.'

The silence was so heavy that it seemed to pulsate with a force of its own. Sarah lay quite still, knowing that whatever she decided now would affect the rest of her life. James would abide by her decision; she knew that as clearly as she knew her own name. If she said no then that would be that, with no recriminations, no cajoling, no threat of any kind. The question was, did she want to say no to him or did she want to see if that lingering dream could be even more beautiful in reality?

It took a courage she hadn't even known she possessed to take the first step along a path she'd sworn she would never tread. Slowly, so slowly that it felt like a part of those dreams, she slid closer to him across the smooth cotton, her hands resting lightly against the warmth of his chest. He drew a deep, shuddery breath, his chest expanding under her fingertips, then slowly dipped his head and brushed her mouth with his in a kiss of such tenderness that she ached.

'Don't be afraid, love. I won't hurt you.' His voice held a note that filled her with warmth. It seemed to steal along her limbs, making her tremble as delicious waves of heat flowed through every cell. James drew her even closer, his hands smoothing her hair back from her hot face, tangling in the thick curls as he pulled her head back so that he could skim kisses down the slender column of her throat. His lips found the tiny pulse that was beating so betrayingly in her neck and lingered while he traced it with the tip of his tongue.

Sarah shivered, unable to hide her reaction to that light, so disturbing touch, and felt him smile with a very masculine sort of triumph. He raised his head, staring quietly into her face before he took her mouth again, this time not softly, not gently, but with a burning need that sent every rational thought spinning out of her head. There was no time for thoughts of the past nor of the future now, just a desire to give whatever it was he wanted from her, and take whatever he gave.

When his hands moved to the tiny buttons that fastened the neck of the plain white gown, she made no move to stop him, made no move at all until she felt the soft brush of his fingertips across the silky smoothness of her breasts. Instinct made her half draw back from his touch, the same instinct that stilled her again when he slowly and deliberately dragged his thumb over the hardening point of her nipple. Sensations seemed to flood through her, and she gasped aloud, a tiny betraying sound that seemed to shock him for a moment. Warm and gentle, his hands rested against the swell of her breasts as though for a moment he was afraid of making any further move that might alarm her. It was obvious that he had meant everything he'd said about taking only what she was willing to give, and her heart swelled with a fierce, almost overwhelming tenderness for this man who cared so much.

Turning her head, she pressed her mouth to his, letting him know by actions what she was too shy to say with words. He groaned deeply, taking the kiss she'd offered and turning it into a sweet seduction of her senses as his tongue slid inside her mouth to tangle with hers in a rhythm that only mirrored what their bodies wanted.

This time there was no hesitation as his fingers began again their sweet trail over her flesh. They smoothed across her breasts, lingering long enough to tease the flesh into throbbing life, then moved on, following the gentle curves of her body, filling her with fire.

'James!' There was no hesitation either now in the way she said his name, no attempt to hide what she was feeling. She wanted him, wanted to feel his hands on her, feel his kiss, feel at last the fierce joy of a man's possession of her. Her hands slid around his neck, her fingers burrowing into the cool silk of his hair while she rained kisses across his face to the lean, hard line of his jaw. He let her kiss him for a moment, his hands still working their delicious magic on her skin, then slowly pulled away just far enough so that he could catch the hem of the long gown and lift it over her head.

'I want to look at you, Sarah. Don't be frightened.' She barely had time to understand what he meant before he flicked on the lamp, bathing them both in its pale glow.

'James, I...' The words of protest died as she saw the way his eyes trailed over her soft pale curves with such hunger in their depths that all her embarrassment faded under the heat of it.

'God, but you're beautiful... so very beautiful!' The words were seemingly wrenched from him, his face contorted with desire as he suddenly bent and pressed his mouth to her breast. Sarah cried out, overwhelmed by the ferocity of the sensations that sprang to life inside her. She'd thought she'd tasted heaven when he'd touched her with his hands, but suddenly she knew that had just been a forerunner to what was to come. When he drew her rigid nipple between his lips and grazed it with his teeth, her hands clenched at her sides, her nails biting into the soft palms as she fought for control, but every sweep of his tongue against her flesh destroyed more and more of that control.

'Touch me, Sarah. Take what I'm so willing to give.' His voice was deep, echoing so softly through the intense silence. Slowly, she unclenched her hands and lifted them to his chest, smoothing her palms back and forth across his body, glorying in the sudden swift intake of breath she felt him take. Under her hands she could feel the heavy throbbing of his heart racing, mirroring the frantic beating of her own, and the very evidence of his need gave her the courage to explore further.

Skin slid under skin, warm and silky, soft yet rough as her fingers traced the perfect contours of his chest, then moved on to his flat belly, stopping when she felt the thickness of hair under her hands once more.

'Don't stop, Sarah. There's nothing to be frightened of in touching me.' He took her hand, guiding it down to his manhood, letting her feel how great his desire for her was.

'James, I...' Her voice was breathy, her face pale with shock and a deep curiosity to learn more about him. She looked down, colouring wildly at what she saw.

'It's how you make me react, Sarah. I want you, and this is the way my body responds to that need.' He pressed her fingers closer to him, watching her face as she felt for the first time the full power of his aroused body. Deep down, a tiny voice was telling her she should be afraid of that power, should remember how once before a man had used it to take what he wanted without a thought for her. But this was different, so very, very different, because this was James who held her now, James whose body sought satisfaction from hers.

She loved him. There was no sound of bells, no brilliant stars, nothing but a sudden acceptance of what she'd tried to hide for some time now. She loved him, and that loving drove the nightmare from her mind and stilled that small voice for good.

When he slid his hand down to seek out the very centre of her, she gasped softly, biting his bare shoulder to hold the trembling shudders at bay for a moment longer, but it was impossible to hold them back for long as he aroused her soft flesh to a throbbing, aching need. Her hips moved, arching towards him, silently begging him for the fulfilment only he could give. He slid between her thighs, taking his full weight on his arms as he stared directly into her eyes. 'Give and take, Sarah... give and take.'

His warm breath sighed into her mouth as he took her lips in a kiss that sent her spinning towards the edge of some deep void. Then his body overwhelmed hers and they became as one, two halves finally joined in a rhythm that sent them both spinning out of control until they were falling, falling over the edge into sweet oblivion.

CHAPTER TEN

IT WAS cool among the trees, the sweetly pungent odour of pine and rotting vegetation filling the morning air.

Sarah leant her head back against the rough bark of a tall pine tree, digging her nails into the spongy damp earth. Was James still sleeping? Or had he woken and even now was wondering where she was? She hugged the thought to her, savouring the coming meeting between them with a greedy pleasure, giving herself up to the sheer joy of what they would say to one another in the clear light of day.

She had no regrets about what had happened, and that surprised her. For a moment she pondered on the fact, then laughed aloud, feeling free for the first time in years. She had given herself to James and by doing so had broken all the chains that had confined her. Now life lay before her, unfettered by any emotional hang-ups. She was free! Free to do anything she wanted, go anywhere she pleased; free to love James MacAllister with the whole of her heart. Free even to go back and tell him that.

She scrambled to her feet, brushing the mossy dirt from her hands, then paused when she heard someone coming along the path towards her. Was it some sixth sense that told her who it was, or was the power of love even greater than she'd imagined it could be? She smiled at her own foolishness, her face alight with joy as she stood in the clearing and waited for him to appear.

'So there you are. I've packed our things. If you want something to eat before we set off then I suggest you get a move on.'

He turned to walk back up the path, leaving Sarah staring after him in shock. She'd not expected sweet words of poetry when they met, but neither had she expected such brusqueness! She ran after him, catching his arm when he made no attempt to slow down. 'James . . . what is it? Why are you acting like this after . . . after last night?' Her cheeks were hot with colour, but she faced him squarely, refusing to believe that he could act in such a way without any reason.

'Last night was last night. Now all I want to do is get on and find my daughter. Understand?'

'No! I don't understand why you're behaving like this. Didn't last night mean anything at all to you? Didn't it?' She shook his arm, her nails biting through the thin cotton shirt he was wearing, but she didn't even notice, consumed with fear as she looked into the granite-hardness of his face.

'Of course it did. I enjoyed it very much, thank you, Sarah. It was remiss of me not to thank you sooner.' The cold mockery made her blanch, but she remained where she was, finding strength born purely out of desperation.

'I don't want thanks. What are you saying, James? That making love to me meant nothing more to you than satisfying a momentary urge, like scratching an itch? I don't believe you!'

'It's up to you what you believe, my sweet, but my advice to you is not to read too much into things. Men and women make love all the time, Sarah. It isn't an earth-shattering event, despite all that romantic non-sense you read in books.'

'And that's all it meant to you? Just a brief, con-venient liaison?' It was hard to disguise the pain that was tearing her heart to shreds, but she needn't have bothered, because he did no more than flick her an im-patient glance.

'What else? If you're thinking of heaping recrimi-nations on my head because you're feeling guilty now, then don't forget that I didn't take anything you weren't willing to give. Grow up, Sarah. See last night for what it was—a learning experience.'

'You really believe that?' She laughed shrilly, the sound echoing through the trees.

'Of course, unless you have some other reason to confess to me.' He glanced at the watch strapped to his broad wrist, impatience in his expression.

'I don't know what you mean.'

'No? It did occur to me that you might have seen last night as a means of softening me up so that I wouldn't carry out my threats against your career.'

'No! It wasn't that at all. It was be-cause...because...' What could she say? How could she admit now that she loved him when she knew that was the last thing he would want to hear?

He smiled coldly, his eyes devoid of any trace of warmth. 'Seeing that you appear to be having difficulty in answering that, I suggest that we agree to leave any further discussions until later. This is only wasting valuable time.'

He turned to stride back along the path, leaving Sarah with tears gathering in her eyes. Last night had been so beautiful, yet it had meant nothing to James at all. What a fool she'd been, a stupid, naïve fool, to have imagined anything different.

In near-despair she trailed after him, brushing the tears from her cheeks before walking along the street. Now that all her hopes had been destroyed she had nothing left apart from pride to see her through the coming hours until she and James would part. It took every ounce of strength to walk up to the café where he was standing, but she managed it, refusing to let him know how hurt she was.

'Right, I'll go inside and settle our bill, if you'll go across to the garage and find out if the car's ready. And don't let them try to put you off, Sarah. Make them understand that we need it now without any further delays.'

His voice was hard, and she smiled bitterly, her eyes lifting to his. 'Oh, don't worry, James. I'm just as anxious as you are to leave!'

Something flickered in his eyes, a fleeting expression that was gone before she had time to determine what had caused it. 'Good. The sooner we can find Catherine, the sooner this whole charade will be over and done with.'

And the sooner you can get rid of me, Sarah thought with an ache of sadness, but she didn't voice it. What was the point? He'd made his views more than plain this morning, so that she could be left in little doubt as to his feelings.

* * *

Sarah stared out of the car window, not seeing the beauty of the countryside as they drove steadily along the road. She felt numb, her whole body frozen by sadness so that nothing seemed to matter any more. James had said little since they'd collected the car, seemingly intent on getting the last leg of the journey over, and Sarah hadn't tried to draw him into conversation. They had nothing left to say to each other, nothing to share apart from the memories of last night, and she didn't want to remember that now.

'I thought we'd head straight into Luchon rather than follow the map. We've lost so much time that it doesn't seem worth doing that now.'

'Whatever you think is best.' Her tone was flat, devoid of feeling from the cold restraint she'd set on her emotions.

He flicked her a half-impatient glance, then turned his attention back to the road to overtake a lorry. 'It seems the most sensible thing to do. Don't you agree?'

'Of course.' She didn't want to talk to him, didn't want to keep on hearing that deep voice which last night had haunted her dreams when she'd finally fallen into an exhausted sleep.

'Look, Sarah, if you're still uptight about what happened last——'

'I don't want to discuss it! Understand? I want to forget that it ever happened, forget what a fool I was!'

She turned to stare out of the window as they drove into the town, blinking back the tears. In the dusty glass she could just make out her reflection, and she smiled bitterly, struck by the irony of what she saw. She had left her hair long and loose about her shoulders that morning, just brushing the silky-soft brown curls back from her face, guided by a desire to look her best when James awoke to see her. That same desire had caused her to wear the one softly feminine outfit she had in her entire wardrobe—a flowing two-piece in soft swirling shades of blue and grey that emphasised her delicate skin and intensified the blue-grey colour of her eyes. How ironic that today of all days she should choose to make herself look as attractive as possible! It wouldn't matter to him if she was dressed in sackcloth and ashes. He had taken what he wanted from her and now was ready to cast her aside without another thought!

'That's fine with me!' The anger in his voice surprised her, and she turned to glance at him, studying the hard set of his jaw, the frown which drew his dark brows together. What did he have to be angry about when it was she who had been made such a fool of?

'What's the matter, James? Annoyed that... Oh!' The gasp was torn from her as he suddenly braked, pulling the car into the kerb. Sarah closed her eyes, feeling her heart pounding in shock, then opened them again just in time to see him thrust the car door open. 'What is it? James!'

'Catherine!' He bit the name out through lips that were white-rimmed with anger, concern darkening his eyes as he glanced back at where Sarah was sitting, stunned by shock. 'Didn't you see her back there on the corner, trying to thumb a lift? I don't know what the hell's been going on, but if that fellow's done anything to hurt her...' He bit off the threat and strode off back along the road.

Slowly Sarah unbuckled the seatbelt, her legs trembling as she climbed out and stared at the two figures standing at the roadside. The end had come so suddenly that she couldn't seem to comprehend what was happening. It was only when James led his daughter back to the car that she managed to get herself together enough to smile faintly at Catherine's stunned expression.

'Miss Marshall!' gasped the girl. 'What are you doing here? Did Dad bring you with him?'

'He did indeed. But never mind about that right now. The main thing is, are you all right?'

Catherine nodded, her eyes shadowed with a mixture of fatigue and strain. 'Yes—just. I... I'm sorry, really sorry. I know I've put you all to a lot of trouble.'

'You have indeed, and when we get somewhere where we can talk I want you to tell me everything, Catherine. Understand? Every single thing!' James glared at his daughter, ignoring the pleading look she gave him. 'I can't believe a child of mine could be so stupid as to pull such a stunt.'

Tears rolled down the girl's cheeks, and instinctively Sarah stepped forward and placed a comforting arm around her shaking shoulders. 'Don't you think that sort of talk can wait until later? This is hardly the time to start berating Catherine when we know nothing about the circumstances.'

He turned on her, his eyes glacial. 'I shall thank you to stay out of this. How I choose to speak to Catherine is my concern. Frankly, Sarah, if I were in your shoes I'd be very careful about what I said.'

The anger she felt was red-hot, melting the numbness in one swift surge. 'And I'll thank you to keep your advice to yourself! I'm a grown woman and quite entitled to express an opinion at any time or in any way I choose! I refuse to stand aside while you upset Catherine even more when it's quite obvious that she's under a great strain.'

'A grown woman, eh?' James slid a mockingly intimate glance over her rigid figure, his eyes lingering with deliberation on the heaving thrust of her breasts under the blue and grey floral fabric. 'I concede that physically you have all the attributes, Sarah, but mentally?' He shook his head, tall and arrogant as he stood there driving the knives deeper and deeper into her broken heart. 'You have a great deal to learn about what being a woman is all about, I'm afraid.'

'How dare you? How dare you stand there and say that after last night?' She was almost shaking with rage, her hands clenching and unclenching at her sides. She wanted to scream and shout, to hit him and make him take that cruel taunt back, but his strength was so much greater than her own. She loved him, yet he cared nothing for her. In a contest of wills he would always win and she would always lose.

'Stop it! Stop it, I say!' Catherine stepped between them, white and shaking. 'I can't take any more arguments... I can't! It was bad enough when we finally got to Philippe's. His mother was furious with him. She even refused to let me stay in the house! She told him he had to get rid of me as fast as he could or she wouldn't ever speak to him again.'

She laughed bitterly, tears streaming down her face. 'Not that it took much persuading to make him agree. I think he'd been having a few second thoughts himself along the way, from the way we argued. But I can't stand to hear you two arguing as well!'

'Don't worry, there won't be any more arguments for you to hear, Catherine. Miss Marshall and I have said all there is to be said.' James's control was phenomenal, showing Sarah all too clearly how easy he found it to block her from his mind. She might have been a stranger, from the cool impersonality of the look he gave her. Just for a moment her gaze lingered on his face, hunger in the depths of her eyes, if he had only taken the time to look; but he didn't. He didn't care a jot about her or her feelings or the love she felt for him. 'Give and take,' he'd said last night. Well, she'd given everything to him, even her heart, and he'd taken it all and tossed it away.

'I just wish I understood why you did it, Catherine. What made you run off like that? Was it something I did, or maybe didn't do?'

'I...perhaps. I don't know really.' Almost desperately the girl looked from her father to Sarah, her expression pleading. 'I didn't mean to upset you, Dad, honestly I didn't. I...I don't know what came over me. It was so stupid!' She swallowed hard. 'It was just something that Miss Marshall said. I thought...I thought... Oh, Dad!' With a wail Catherine flung herself into her father's arms and sobbed.

He held her tightly, his hand smoothing down her back in a gesture of comfort, but as he looked up and met Sarah's eyes above his daughter's bowed head there was no gentleness in his expression, just a harsh condemnation. And every last lingering spark of hope that somehow they could work things out between them faded.

Sarah turned away to climb back into the car, aching with a pain that drove so deep that she felt it would tear her apart. Not only had she to contend with the knowledge of how James had used her but with the fact that he would always blame her now for what had happened. She would be damned forever in his eyes, and nothing she could say would ever change his opinion of her. Suddenly she didn't know if she would be able to cope.

The noise of excited chatter echoed along the quiet corridor, then faded abruptly as one of the girls whispered a warning. Sarah paused outside the door to the room Catherine was sharing with two other girls, then walked on, her footsteps dragging as she made her way to her own room.

She closed the door and stared round, studying the once familiar furnishings. Had it really only been a matter of days since she was last in this room? She knew it was, yet so much time seemed to have elapsed since that night when James had pushed his way into the room and disrupted the whole of her life. She sighed deeply, realising that she'd just done the one thing she'd promised herself not to do in thinking about him, but it was impossible not to, especially as he had been forced to spend the night in the hotel with the rest of the school party.

Sarah had passed him in the hall on her way out from dinner and heard his obvious annoyance at not being able to get seats for him and Catherine on a plane back that night. She had almost been tempted to stop just to say something or maybe offer help, but he'd cut her dead. It had taken all her composure to carry on up the stairs and not break down at that. All she could cling to now was the thought that after tomorrow she wouldn't be forced to meet him again. It was a very cold sort of comfort.

The door opened abruptly, the sound making her swing round in surprise to stare at the tall figure who'd come in. Just for a second everything stilled, as though the world was holding its breath . . . waiting. Then James closed the door and she snapped back to life.

'Get out!'

He smiled coldly, crossing the room to stare out of the window before flicking a haughty look over his shoulder. 'I imagine it's a little late for all that righteous indignation now, Sarah. This is hardly the first time that you and I have been alone together in a bedroom, so spare me that, please.'

'What do you want?' She could feel herself starting to shake, feel the tension humming along her nerves, drawing them so tight that at any moment she feared she would shatter into a thousand tiny pieces.

'I could hardly leave in the morning without saying goodbye, could I? Not after all we've shared these past few days.'

His tone whipped the colour back into her ashen face. It was agony to have him speak to her like that, with so much contempt, but she refused to show him how much he could hurt her with his cruel barbs. 'So a night in bed earns a show of good manners, does it? I'm flattered, James, that you should even bother to spare me that much of your time. I must have acquitted myself better than I imagined.'

His nostrils flared, colour running in a thin red line along his high cheekbones. 'I didn't come here to swap insults, Sarah.'

'No? Then why did you come?' She tilted her head, glad now that she hadn't bothered to change out of the flattering outfit. She needed the confidence it gave her, needed it to fight this final battle. 'So no insults, eh? Makes me wonder exactly what it is you want at this late hour.' She glanced at her watch, then back at him, feeling her heart pounding. She shouldn't goad him like this, shouldn't quite deliberately try to arouse his anger, but the temptation was too great to resist. 'Surely it couldn't be that you've come back for seconds?' She let her gaze trail over him as he stood there in an insulting inspection, then smiled with false brightness. 'Well, thank you, but no, thank you. Once was enough, James.'

She turned her back on him to walk to the door and usher him from the room, but she got no more than a couple of steps before he had her in his arms. 'Don't you turn your back on me, lady, after saying that!'

'Why? Does it offend your ego that I could refuse?' She tossed her head, sending the pale curls tumbling over her shoulder, her eyes glittering. 'Oh, I enjoyed it last night, James. You're a skilled and able lover, so if you need a reference don't hesitate to contact me. But as to a repeat performance, I think I shall pass. Now please let me go.'

'Let you go? Oh, you protest very prettily, but why do I get the impression that your heart isn't in it, Sarah?' He slid his arms further around her, pulling her close against the hard strength of his body. 'Are you sure that's what you really want?'

'Yes! My God, but I never fully realised before just how conceited you are! You heard what I said—now do it!'

'Why should I when I'm sure I could change your mind?' He bent and brushed her mouth with his, but she turned her head, consumed with pain that he should treat her so.

'I meant it, James,' she said quietly. 'Let me go now.'

'And what if I refuse? Then what will you do, Miss Marshall? Protest some more, or give yourself up to what you know you want—another few hours in my arms?' He smiled coldly, watching the hectic colour flooding her face before allowing his gaze to drop to the parted fullness of her mouth.

Suddenly Sarah knew that this had moved beyond a mere tussle of wills. He meant what he said, meant that he would use every trick or skill he possessed to get her into his arms and into bed. For a moment she felt dizzy with just the thought of it, until sanity returned with a chilling force. Why did he now want to make love to her when before he'd barely tolerated her presence? Because he was consumed by a fresh desire for her? Or because she had pricked his huge ego by what she'd said before?

She tore herself out of his arms, taking him by surprise. 'I said no and I meant no, James. Is that so hard to understand? Or do you too suffer from that same affliction so many men suffer from...strategic deafness?' She laughed brittly. 'Ah, I see that surprises you. Why? Didn't you imagine that any other man could have used the same tactics with me? But of course not. Not poor frumpish Sarah Marshall, the old-maid schoolteacher. What would she know about men? I expect you thought you were doing me a favour last night, didn't you? Making love to me, giving me a few memories to store up for my old age?'

She laughed again, a trace of hysteria in the sound. She bit her lip, shaking her head when he made as if to touch her. 'No! I don't want you to touch me. You had your fun last night, so let's call it quits, shall we, and end this whole messy incident with dignity?'

She turned to open the door, wanting to get him out of the room before she broke down completely, but he made no attempt to leave. 'None of this would ever have happened if you'd faced up to whatever it is that still haunts you, Sarah. You can't keep on hiding from the past. You've seen what effect it can have, not only on yourself but others as well. If we're talking home truths now then why not add a few others to the list and clear the air once and for all?'

Her hands shook as she gripped the door so tightly that her fingers ached from the pressure. 'What happened in my past is none of your damned business!'

'Isn't it?' With a speed that was startling James took the door from her and closed it firmly, his eyes burning as they met hers. 'I'd say it was very much my business. It was my daughter whom you influenced in some way.' He held his hand up to forestall her. 'Don't bother, I've heard it all before, but I also heard what Catherine said earlier when I asked her why she'd run away. Granted she hasn't fully explained, but it was clear that you were to blame as I'd suspected. I think I deserve some answers, don't you?'

'You deserve nothing, James...nothing, unless you want to count last night as some sort of a payment! The past is my business; it has nothing to do with you or anyone!'

'That's where you're wrong!' His anger was mounting, then he seemed to make a conscious effort to control it. 'We shared so much last night, Sarah, so why is it so hard to share this huge secret as well?'

There was a deliberate note of challenge in the coldly mocking voice that suddenly tipped her over the edge. All day long she'd tried to keep a rein on the agony that was ripping her to shreds, but now she snapped. She moved away from the door, her actions stiff and uncoordinated, her hands twisted into the folds of the skirt as all the barriers finally fell and the past rushed back to merge in one sickening flood with the present.

'So you want to share it, do you, James? Want to hear what made me into the woman I am today?' She laughed hollowly, unaware of the way he flinched at the bitterness in her voice. 'What makes Miss Marshall such a prim old maid? Oh, I've often heard that question being asked, but I've never answered it until today—but maybe you're right about it being time to clear the air.' She looked up and met his eyes, her face pale but strangely composed. 'I was raped when I was twenty. That's the secret I've been so loath to share with anyone, so consider yourself highly honoured.'

'Sarah! I...' She'd never seen James at a loss for words before. He looked as though he'd been hit, his face set into grim lines, his eyes so dark that it was impossible to read anything in them. What was he thinking, feeling? Disgust, pity, contempt? She had no idea, and no desire to find out.

'You what? Are glad that I told you, shared this secret? Or maybe you'd like to hear a few of the more salacious details? Well, I'm very sorry, James, but that's all I think you need to——' Sarah broke off abruptly as he crossed the couple of feet that separated them and caught her by the shoulders, his fingers bruising.

'Stop that! Of course I don't want to hear any details!' He shook her just once, then stared down at where his hands were holding her shoulders. Slowly he loosened his grip and stepped back, running a hand through his dark hair as though he was suddenly afraid to touch her. Why? Because he couldn't bear the thought of touching her now that he knew the truth?

Tears misted her eyes and she walked away to stare sightlessly out of the window, wishing as she had wished so many times before that she could erase the past, but of course she couldn't. She couldn't change what had happened, she could only learn to live with it. Now it seemed an even more difficult task.

'I'm sorry, Sarah.' The note in his voice made her heart ache, and she clenched her hands until her nails bit into her palms to hold on to what little was left of her control. Did he mean he was sorry about what had happened, or about making her tell him about it? She didn't know, and even when she heard the soft sound of the door opening she didn't try to ask him. She let him leave without a word because there was no word she could think of that would stop him.

CHAPTER ELEVEN

'I JUST want to thank you all for the party and the presents and—oh, well, everything!' Stephanie Jacobs smiled round at the group, then wiped a few tears from her cheeks as she raised her glass. 'I propose a toast to the school and the girls, and especially to Sarah, who gave me the courage to make the break at last after talking about it for so long!'

Sarah smiled, joining the other teachers in raising her glass. The wine was cold, tingling on her palate as she took a drink. Abruptly she set the glass down on the table and moved away to look out of the staffroom window, but she saw little of the countryside that stretched away to the distance beyond the limits of the school playing fields. What she saw was mountains, wild, barely tamed, glowing softly pink in the morning sunlight. She'd not drunk wine since that time she and James had spent in the Pyrenees, and now all the memories she'd tried to blank out came rushing back.

'Sarah? Are you all right?' Stephanie broke away from the group to come and stand beside her, her pretty face filled with concern, and Sarah tried her best to smile.

'Of course. Just daydreaming, that's all.'

'About James MacAllister?' The younger woman smiled at Sarah's start of surprise. 'Oh, don't bother trying to deny it, Sarah. You and I have become good friends in the past few weeks, and I've noticed how you close up at odd times, as though you're remembering something painful. Did you fall in love with him when you were off looking for Catherine?'

'I...' Sarah nodded, her face strained. 'Stupid, isn't it? You'd think a woman of my age would know better.'

'Age has nothing to do with it! There isn't a woman born who "knows better" when good old Cupid shoots his arrow. What I can't understand is why you don't follow the advice you gave me when I was trying to make up my mind to give up my job and see something of the world. You told me to always look to the future and never find yourself in the position whereby you regret not doing something. It seems sound advice in this case too.'

'So what do you suggest? That I should telephone him and inform him that I just happen to be madly in love with him?' Sarah shook her head, her soft brown hair glinting in the sunlight that spilled through the window. 'I don't think so! James MacAllister isn't the least concerned about how I feel.'

'Is that right?' Stephanie took a swallow of her wine, the light of battle shining in her blue eyes. 'Then how come he changed his mind about removing Catherine from school? And how come he didn't pursue his intention to drive you out of teaching? He doesn't care? Huh!'

'He probably didn't think it worth the effort,' said Sarah flatly. 'And as for leaving Catherine here, I imagine she had some influence over that decision. I think she's enjoyed the boost it gave to her standing among the other girls, so I'm sure she refused to change schools.'

'And you fondly imagine that James MacAllister, the *same* James MacAllister who looked as though he'd never considered anyone else's view in his life when I saw him, really bowed to a fifteen-year-old's wishes?' Stephanie shook her head, her black hair swinging forward across her face before she impatiently pushed it back. 'No way! He did it because of you, Sarah. Because he cares!' She set her glass down, grimacing as the bell marking the afternoon's classes rang. 'Well, back to the grindstone, then. Three more classes and then that's it for me. No more teaching, if things work out as planned. But promise me you'll think about what I said, Sarah.' She hugged her impulsively. 'Don't be afraid to go after what you want. Life is just too short.'

She was gone before Sarah could answer. Slowly she turned away from the window, wishing it were all as simple as Stephanie seemed to think it was. She could just imagine James's reaction if she did phone him and confess that she was in love with him and that she felt as though life wasn't worth living without him. He would either cut her dead with that cold, bruising mockery or laugh his head off, and she couldn't cope with either. It was eight weeks since she'd seen him, eight long, lonely weeks which hadn't lessened the pain. All she wanted now was to live her life as best she could, sustained by the memories of those too brief days they'd had together.

The third-year class was restless, touched with holiday fever, so that it took all Sarah's skill to hold their interest. Settling them down in groups with a French crossword she'd spent most of the previous evening devising, she ignored the whispered comments and laughter, understanding their excitement at the thought of the coming summer break even though she didn't share it. At least while she was teaching she could keep her mind busy, but the thought of all the empty days filled her with near-despair. She closed her eyes against the pain, then opened them abruptly as the classroom door was flung open.

'James!' Was that really her voice saying his name in that breathless, disbelieving tone? Was it really James standing there in the doorway? She shook her head, wondering if she was hallucinating from the strain she'd been working under, but then he spoke and she knew he was real.

'I need to speak to you, Sarah.'

It was just like old times; there was that same note of steely arrogance in his voice, that same certainty that she would meekly fall in with his wishes! Sarah stood up, her face cold as she stared back at him and shook her head. 'Quite apart from the fact that I have no idea what we have to talk about, it's obviously out of the question right now. I happen to be teaching a class, Mr MacAllister, so I shall be grateful if you'd leave.'

'Again? You seem to make a habit out of asking me to leave, Sarah. It could become boring if you aren't careful.' He looked round, his eyes skimming the curious, upturned faces of the girls, who had abandoned the crossword in favour of this more interesting turn of events. 'Right, who's form prefect here?'

A girl at the back of the class raised her hand. 'Me, sir.'

'Right, you're in charge until Miss Marshall gets back. Understand?'

'James!' There was no breathless note to Sarah's voice now, just a red-hot anger at his incredible high-handedness. 'I really don't have any idea why you should imagine you can come in here and start giving orders, but let me tell you I won't stand for it! Now please leave.'

'I think not. I made the mistake of leaving once before and I have no intention of making the same mistake again.' He glanced round, then calmly walked over to a vacant chair and sat down. 'I shall wait until you're free to talk to me, Sarah. Just carry on as though I'm not here.'

If only! If only she could pretend that he wasn't in the same room, so close that all it would take was a few short steps and she could touch him. Her fingers itched with the desire to feel his skin under hers and she sat down abruptly, knowing that for now at least she was beaten. This was neither the time nor the place to start a discussion which would probably lead to one of their frequent quarrels.

'Right then, girls, carry on with what you were doing, and if anyone finds herself stuck then please ask. There may be one or two words in the piece that you're unfamiliar with.' Sarah was pleased to hear how steady her voice sounded, belying the fact that she felt as though someone was slowly and methodically squeezing all the air out of her lungs. She could feel James watching her, actually *feel* that dark-eyed stare as though it was a physical touch.

Unbidden, her eyes lifted to where he was sitting, and her heart seemed to stop as she caught the expression of warmth and tenderness on his face. Time seemed to hang suspended for a tense moment as they stared at each other, then one of the pupils asked a question and everything slipped back into place.

'Three across, Miss Marshall—a mountainous region that forms a natural frontier. We can't think what it is. Can you give us another clue?'

Why had she included that in the crossword? Had her thoughts been so centred on James that even when she was supposedly working she'd found it impossible to blot him from her mind? 'I...' Embarrassment stole the words from her as she looked across the room and saw him smiling. He knew! Knew that she'd found it impossible to forget him and what they had shared.

'Try Pyrenees—it should fit. I imagine that's the region Miss Marshall was thinking about when she worked the crossword out.'

His deep voice held a wealth of meaning as he spoke, the warm tones sending a shudder through Sarah. She jumped to her feet, almost upsetting her chair in her haste, her cheeks filling with colour as she heard him laugh softly. 'I'll just write a few words on the blackboard that you might have trouble spelling.'

She picked up the chalk and turned her back on the class, then jumped when James spoke again, his voice even warmer this time, if that was possible.

'Could you spell something for me, please? I love you...in French, of course.'

The chalk screeched against the board as her hand slipped, then fell from her nerveless fingers. Automatically, Sarah bent to retrieve it, feeling the blood rushing to her head.

'It's *Je t'aime*, if I'm not mistaken, isn't it, Miss Marshall?' He laughed deeply, his eyes centring on her flushed face. 'I'm not certain if that's the correct way to say it; maybe you could repeat it for me before you write it down?'

Why was he doing this? Why was he deliberately making it sound as though he was saying he loved her? She clenched the chalk in her fingers, conscious that the girls were hanging on to every word. 'That's quite right, Mr MacAllister. There's nothing wrong with your pronunciation.' Her voice was husky, betraying her agitation, and he smiled gently, his dark eyes locking calmly to hers.

'I'm still not one hundred per cent sure that I have the accent right, though, Miss Marshall. So please won't you say it for me so that I can check?'

Was it a game or some new way to torment her? Sarah had no idea, and she suddenly didn't care as she stared across the room into his face. She loved him! It didn't matter what language it was said in, it would still be the same; still sound just as marvellous to be able to say it to him.

'*Je t'aime.*' Her voice barely broke the hush that had fallen over the group. She drew in a sharp little breath, feeling her heart thundering inside her chest. '*Je t'aime*, Mr MacAllister,' she repeated slowly, looking straight at him with everything she felt shining in her eyes.

He seemed to catch his breath, his face contracting into rigid lines almost of pain before he suddenly relaxed and smiled, a smile that held such warmth that she felt all the coldness start to melt. '*Je t'aime*, Miss Marshall. How does that sound?'

'I . . . You . . . Marvellous, absolutely marvellous!'

'I hoped it would.' He stood up and walked over to her, taking the chalk from her shaking hands and tossing it carelessly aside before glancing round at the class, who were sitting there enthralled. 'Now, girls, I know I can rely on you all to behave while I have a private word with your teacher. Don't let me down, now.'

Taking Sarah by the arm, he led her from the room, closing the door behind them and cutting off the excited chatter that had broken out. 'Where to? We need somewhere we can talk, Sarah.'

'I...' She blinked rapidly, wondering if she was dreaming. This just couldn't be happening! James couldn't really be here, abducting her from the classroom!

'Somewhere quiet, Sarah, and very, very private for what I have in mind.' His voice was husky with desire, his dark eyes filled with a message that she would have had to be blind not to see, and she shivered violently.

'James, this is madness! You can't come in here and drag me out of the classroom! The girls need me.'

'Not half as much as I need you, my sweet.' James turned her into his arms, lifting her face so that he could brush her mouth with his in a kiss of such aching tenderness that her knees seemed to give way and she would have fallen if he hadn't steadied her.

'I made a mistake, Sarah, in leaving you that night. It's something I've regretted every minute of every single day since, and I won't let it ever happen again. I love you... *Je t'aime*. I'll tell you it every damned way you like if you'll agree to give me a second chance and explain why I acted the way I did that morning, and why I left your room that night. So please tell me where we can go to talk, otherwise I swear that I'll take matters into my own hands!' He looked round the quiet corridor, smiling faintly. 'How do you think your esteemed headmistress would feel about one of her staff being made love to in the middle of the corridor?'

'James! You wouldn't! I... Do you mean it? Do you really love me?'

He brushed his lips across hers. 'I do, Sarah. I honestly and truly do, and I can't think of anything I want more than to show you how much.' He eased her against him, letting her feel his need of her, then reluctantly let her go. 'However, this really isn't the place for that, is it?'

'I...' She couldn't seem to think straight any longer, couldn't seem to separate one sensible thought from the crazy jumble whirling in her head. James loved her! It was the answer to all her prayers, and almost impossible to believe.

He seemed to understand her confusion, smiling tenderly as he took her hand and led her along the corridor and out of the side-door to where his car was parked. 'Get in, love. We'll go somewhere we can talk.' He bent and kissed her hard, his lips lingering in a caress that did little to ease the crazy confusion in her mind. Drawing back, he studied her stunned expression, then smiled with an entirely masculine satisfaction as he slammed the door and walked round the car to slide behind the wheel.

'I... Where are we going, James?' Sarah asked huskily, her eyes loving him.

'Just a little way along the road by the river. It should be quiet there, and private away from all those curious eyes.' He nodded towards the school as he started the engine, laughing at Sarah's shocked gasp as she suddenly realised that most of her abandoned class were watching out of the window and must have seen James kiss her. 'Oh, no! Whatever will they think?'

'I imagine they'll understand completely, Sarah. In my experience teenage girls are very adept at reading the signs!'

'That's what worries me! This is hardly setting them a good example, is it? Letting you kiss me here right in front of them!'

He turned the car off the road, drawing it to a halt on the riverbank. 'Frankly, Sarah, I couldn't give a damn what sort of an example we're setting them. They're not my concern, you are! Now come here and let me kiss you properly before I go mad!'

He pulled her into his arms and kissed her with a burning passion, his mouth seeking a response she was more than willing to give. When at last he let her go he was trembling almost as hard as she was, his eyes feverish with desire. Sarah smoothed a hand lovingly down his cheek, shuddering when he turned his head and nipped her palm.

'I never dreamt this would happen, James,' she said softly. 'I thought it was all over between us, especially after what I told you that night.'

'So did I, although not for the reason I think you mean.' He lifted her face and looked straight into her eyes. 'The fact that you were raped doesn't affect the way I feel about you, Sarah. Perhaps I gave you the impression that it did when I left so abruptly, but all I can say is that I was so shocked by the revelation and so ashamed of the way I'd behaved that I didn't know how to handle it. I wish you'd told me sooner, then I would never have pushed you so hard.'

'No, you were right to do it.' She kissed him quickly on the mouth, hating to see the pain on his face. 'The same as you were right about me being an emotional cripple.' She smiled sadly when he started to protest, smoothing a finger against his lips to stem the words. 'No, don't. I *had* allowed it to rule my life, when what I should have done was put it behind me.'

'That's probably easier said than done. I can only begin to imagine what you went through.' He caught her hands, holding them tight between both of his. 'Can you tell me what happened, Sarah? Or is it still too painful for you?'

'Not any longer. Oh, I won't ever be able to forget what happened, but it won't dominate my life any longer the way it has done these past years.' She gazed past him, letting her mind roll back. 'I was just turned twenty when it happened, in my third year at university and enjoying life. Then my parents were killed in a car crash on their way to visit me one weekend. I was completely devastated, because as an only child I'd always been so close to them. Losing them both like that was a bitter blow.

'My work started to suffer because of it, and one of my tutors offered to give me extra tuition to help me catch up.' She laughed bitterly, unaware of the way James's jaw clenched in anger. 'It seems that French tuition wasn't quite all he had in mind! I was at a low ebb, aware that I was falling behind, and I was grateful for his offer. He seemed to be eager to help me get over my loss too, so that when he invited me to stay the weekend at his house I readily agreed.'

She glanced at James, realising for the first time that this was almost as painful for him as it was for her. 'Shall I go on, or would it be better if I stopped now?'

He shook his head, squeezing her fingers hard. 'I want to hear it all, Sarah, if you want to tell me. I want to put it all behind us once and for all.'

She nodded, understanding what he meant. Only by telling him what had happened could she finally break all links with the past. 'He... he was married, you see, so I thought it would be quite in order to accept his invitation, but unfortunately he'd omitted to tell me that his wife would be away. I... I won't go into all the unsavoury details, but by the time I'd found out the truth it was too late. He... he raped me in his house, then laughed when I told him I was going to the police. He said that no one would ever believe that I hadn't been a willing participant and that it would be my name that would be dragged through the mud.' Tears filled her eyes and she blinked them away, clinging hold of James's hands. 'In the end I didn't tell anyone, James. He got away with it because I was afraid he'd be proved right!'

'Don't! Don't blame yourself, Sarah. Who knows what might have happened?' James struck his fist against the dashboard, his expression murderous. 'I wish to hell I could get my hands on him. I'd make him pay for what he did to you!'

'It's all in the past now. It no longer matters... not if you meant what you said about it making no difference to you.' Sarah closed her eyes, suddenly afraid. 'I was always terrified of anyone finding out in case...

You weren't disgusted that night, were you, James? I need to know the truth.'

'No! Is that what you thought?' Pain crossed his face. 'It wasn't like that. I can't explain really how I felt. It was a mixture of anger and shock and a sense of self-disgust that I'd pushed you into telling me something you were obviously so loath to tell. I'd done nothing but goad you right from the beginning, but I never suspected the truth. Yet in a way it explained so much about the way you behaved and the reasons why such a beautiful woman should do her damnedest to hide her beauty.'

'Beautiful? Me?'

He smiled as he drew her into his arms and kissed her softly. 'You. Don't look so surprised. I was smitten from the first moment I met you at that parents' day. You were so lovely, with your delicate skin and your soft hair, yet you did your best to hide it.' He slid his hand into her hair to pull out the pins and winnow the silky curls through his fingers. 'I've ached many a night to do this again, Sarah, the same as I've ached when I remembered how you looked that morning lying next to me in bed with your hair spread over the pillows.'

'Have you? I thought you were still asleep when I got up.' The touch of his hands was making her giddy, but she made herself concentrate, knowing he was determined to clear everything up.

'I pretended I was, but I'd woken hours before and just lay there watching you.'

'Why didn't you say something?' Her eyes were clouded with pain. 'And why were you so cruel later in the wood? I . . . I thought you'd had what you wanted from me and that was that.'

'That's how I hoped it would be.' He smiled with more than a trace of wryness when he heard her shocked gasp. 'But it just shows how wrong a man can be. I was deliberately cruel that morning because I didn't trust myself to be anything else. I'd hoped that once we'd made love then I'd get you out of my system, but I woke up and saw you and I knew that wasn't going to be so. I was afraid, Sarah. That's the real truth of the situation.'

'Afraid? What of?'

'You!' He laughed deeply, his voice rumbling deliciously to send trickles of heat along her veins, and she stirred restlessly in his arms, nestling closer. 'Keep that up, lady, and I shall never get to the end of this sorry tale!'

Sarah smiled cheekily, tilting her head back to nip his chin in a mock-threatening caress. 'No way, Mr MacAllister! I intend to hear all of it, understand? Now!'

'And later? What happens then?' He smiled as she blushed. 'We'll leave that for now, shall we? I was afraid because I suddenly realised that I was falling in love with you. It wasn't just sexual attraction any more. I'd sworn when Ruth died that I'd never fall into that trap again, and yet there I was, in so deep I panicked.'

'You must have loved her a lot.' There was no way she could disguise the pain she felt at the thought, and she heard him sigh.

'I did. I won't lie and say differently, Sarah, but what I felt for Ruth is in the past, just a memory now. It doesn't affect the way I feel about you. It just made me afraid to face up to how I felt. I'd sworn never to go through the trauma of allowing myself to fall in love only to lose that person again. I'm not saying I've lived like a monk all these years—far from it. But the women I chose knew the score. There was never any emotional involvement. Then along you came and nearly drove me crazy with your sharp little comments about how I treated Catherine, your maddening primness and your infuriating attraction! I knew from the first that you were trouble, and I was right. You were and are big trouble, Miss Marshall.'

'Well, thank you very much!' She glared with mock-annoyance, then smiled suddenly. 'I don't think I've had a nicer compliment! Staid, old-maid Miss Marshall...big trouble!'

'Mmm—well, I don't think that description is going to be true for long. Now that I've finally found the courage to admit to my feelings I don't intend to leave you as Miss anything for very long.'

Sarah took a deep breath and counted to ten. 'Do you call that a proposal? Forget it!'

'What?'

'You heard me, Mr MacAllister! If that was supposed to be a proposal of marriage then it was a pitiful effort. Either try again, or forget it!'

'Why, you little...' James bit off the exclamation, tilting her face so that he could kiss her with masterful possession, not letting her go until she was quite breathless. He smiled into her dreamy eyes, smoothing a long finger over her kiss-swollen mouth. 'You will marry me, won't you, Sarah? I don't think I can go on without you much longer. I've nearly gone crazy these past weeks trying to convince myself I'd be better off without you in my life, but it's all been one huge lie. I need you, Sarah!'

She smiled back at him, loving him more than she could tell him in just words. 'If that's what you want, James.'

'It is. I love you, Sarah. I want you in my life forever.'

'And I love you too,' she whispered softly. 'I can't think of anything I want more than to be your wife and live with you.' She paused, struck by a sudden unsettling thought. 'How about Catherine? Do you think she'll like the idea of me being married to her father?'

'She's delighted.' He saw her frown and laughed, quite unabashed. 'I phoned her last night and told her I was coming down here today and wouldn't be leaving until you'd agreed to marry me. She said, and I quote, "It's about time you made an honest woman of Miss Marshall!"'

'What? James! You never told her about what happened between us, about us...us...'

'Sleeping together? No, my sweet, not in so many words. However, Catherine seems to have grown up, thanks to her own escapades, and I think she found it simple to put two and two together.'

'Then how could I refuse? It would set her such a bad example.' Sarah sobered. 'I've spoken to her about what happened, but she's not told me much other than she knew almost at once that she'd made a mistake. Thank goodness she had the sense to make that plain to Philippe, which probably explains why he was more than willing to leave her in Luchon after his mother objected to her being taken to his house.' She swallowed hard, suddenly afraid to disturb their happiness. 'If I was to blame in any way for what happened then I'm sorry, James.'

'You were.' He laughed when he heard her startled gasp. 'But so was I, Sarah. Catherine and I have had several long talks lately, starting on the flight back to Britain from Paris. She finally came out and admitted that she'd formed the idea that I didn't care about her because I'd been so busy with my work. It shook me. I... I hadn't realised what I'd been doing, but I made her understand that I love her very much. In the end it was quite simple. I only wish we'd talked about how we felt sooner.'

'I'm glad it's cleared up, but how did I feature in what happened? Was it something I said? I shall never forgive myself if I really was to blame.'

'Evidently it was just a passing comment you made during a lesson. You were all translating some French love poems, and you remarked that love is the most important of all human emotions, something so precious that it should take precedence over everything else. She must have taken it to heart because she was feeling so unhappy at my seeming lack of concern and used it as the means to justify going off with Philippe. She thought he loved her, but unfortunately, or fortunately, depending on your view, she found out that wasn't so. Luckily it all turned out all right in the end, and I think it's taught Catherine a few lessons she won't forget.'

'Oh, James. I never realised something so innocuous could have that effect. I shall have to be more careful.'

'Mmm, I think it depends on the pupil. Love should come before everything else?' He smiled down at her, his eyes holding a message that made her feel hot and cold all at once. He bent and kissed her softly, drawing back before she could respond, leaving her hungry for the taste of him. 'I think I could enjoy that sort of a lesson, teacher.'

She coloured delicately. 'I think you'd make the better teacher in this instance.'

'Think so?' James bent towards her again, his warm breath making her ache with longing. 'You could be right. Shall we try lesson number one, then if you prove to be an apt pupil we can progress from there?'

Sarah smiled as his mouth settled on hers, her hands linking around his neck. She didn't know about being an apt pupil. She had the feeling that she might need an awful lot of teaching, plus a lot of revision on some of the finer points!

Next Month's Romances

Each month you can choose from a wide variety of romance with Mills & Boon. Below are the new titles to look out for next month, why not ask either Mills & Boon Reader Service or your Newsagent to reserve you a copy of the titles you want to buy – just tick the titles you would like and either post to Reader Service or take it to any Newsagent and ask them to order your books.

Please save me the following titles:	Please tick	√
TO TAME A WILD HEART	Emma Darcy	
ISLAND ENCHANTMENT	Robyn Donald	
A VALENTINE FOR DAISY	Betty Neels	
PRACTISE TO DECEIVE	Sally Wentworth	
FLAME ON THE HORIZON	Daphne Clair	
ROMAN SPRING	Sandra Marton	
OVE OR NOTHING	Natalie Fox	
LOSE CAPTIVITY	Elizabeth Power	
OTAL POSSESSION	Kathryn Ross	
ST LADY	Lee Wilkinson	
T-WRAPPED	Victoria Gordon	
T SUCH A STRANGER	Liza Hadley	
LOURS OF LOVE	Rosalie Henaghan	
CHECKMATE	Peggy Nicholson	
TOMORROW'S MAN	Sue Peters	
OF RASCALS AND RAINBOWS	Marcella Thompson	

If you would like to order these books in addition to your regular subscription from Mills & Boon Reader Service please send £1.80 per title to: Mills & Boon Reader Service, Freepost, P.O. Box 236, Croydon, Surrey, CR9 9EL, quote your Subscriber No:................................. (If applicable) and complete the name and address details below. Alternatively, these books are available from many local Newsagents including W.H.Smith, J.Menzies, Martins and other paperback stockists from 5 November 1993.

Name:...

Address:...

....Post Code:.........................

To Retailer: If you would like to stock M&B books please contact your regular book/magazine wholesaler for details.

You may be mailed with offers from other reputable companies as a result of this application. If you would rather not take advantage of these opportunities please tick box ☐